D1613278

STANIER 4-6-0s
AT WORK

STANIER 4-6-0s AT WORK

A.J.POWELL

44925

IA
LONDON
IAN ALLAN LTD

Contents

Previous page: The 15.10 Edinburgh connection from Carstairs is made by Class 5 No 44925 with a light three-coach set in 1966, passing Dolphinton Junction box, the eastern corner of the Carstairs triangle. *W. A. C. Smith*

Below right: The 1 in 37.7 gradient of the Lickey Incline clearly shows in this study of No 45654 *Hood* **as she clears the summit at Blackwell in August 1960, banked in rear by a WR '94' class 0-6-0T, with a 12-coach Bristol- Bradford express. The engine is being worked at about 60% cutoff.** *Derek Cross*

Front endpaper: No 44999 in immaculate condition heads an express out of Edinburgh Princes St about 1948. Judging by the polished buffers, drawhook and shackle she has been specially prepared for a Royal Train. *Ian Allan Library*

Rear endpaper: 'Jubilee' No 45705 *Seahorse* **is gathering speed again as she emerges from Blea Moor Tunnel with the 10-coach 09.20 Manchester Victoria- Glasgow Central in July 1964.** *Paul Riley*

Cover: 'Jubilee' class 4-6-0 No 5602 *British Honduras* **heads the northbound 'Devonian' through snow covered countryside near Westerleigh in January 1939.** *Painting by George F. Heiron*

First published 1983

ISBN 0 7110 1342 X

All rights reserved. No part of this book may be reproduced or transmitted in any form or by any means, electronic or mechanical, including photo- copying, recording or by any information storage and retrieval system, without permission from the Publisher in writing.

© A. J. Powell, 1983

Published by Ian Allan Ltd, Shepperton, Surrey; and printed by Ian Allan Printing Ltd at their works at Coombelands in Runnymede, England.

Preface

In using the title '...at Work', I have attempted to present a comprehensive picture of the Stanier 4-6-0s in the fields of design, performance on the road, and maintenance. No locomotive can be said to be wholly successful unless it can stand up to scrutiny in all these aspects of its work. For much of the prewar period I have necessarily drawn on a wide variety of contemporary sources, but the postwar years have very largely been covered from personal experience in a variety of posts related to these three fields. These involved tens of thousands of miles of travel on the footplate under all conditions, and much time in motive power depots and main works in the follow-up of mechanical performance.

Throughout, I have used the generic class names of 'Jubilees' and (relating to their immediate predecessors) 'Patriots', while recognising that these engines did not receive these class titles from their inception. In referring to train times, I have thought it reasonable to use the 24-hour clock, now in almost universal use by transport undertakings. I have, however, used the original power classification of '5XP' for the 'Jubilees' in all matters up to the change of '6P' in 1951, largely because of its use in official reports being quoted.

I am very conscious that a considerable amount of text is taken up with the programmes of testing which these engines underwent, and hope that the reader will not find this disproportionate. Testing played such an important part in their development into the capable machines they became, and was so relevant to their work and in illuminating various features of their day-to-day operation, that it seemed essential to give it adequate treatment.

In this connection the terms 'drawbar horsepower' (DBHP) and 'equivalent drawbar horsepower' (EDBHP) have been extensively used. For those not familiar with locomotive performance testing, it may be helpful to explain here that DBHP relates the actual drawbar pull at the tender, and the speed, to show the horsepower applied to the train, and on level track this represents the full production of usable power for 'commercial' purposes. On rising gradients, however, a proportion of this power has to be devoted to

getting the engine and tender up the gradient, leaving less available at the drawbar. To enable a uniform assessment to be made, the EDBHP brings together the actual (reduced) DBHP plus the horsepower involved in getting engine and tender up the gradient, thus showing the true rate at which the engine is working.

In the preparation of this book I gratefully acknowledge help from a variety of sources. Phil Atkins, the Librarian at the National Railway museum, York, and his staff have been tireless in their pursuit of reports and remaining documentation, drawings and references from their resources. The Scottish Record Office, Edinburgh have also been very helpful. One-time colleagues have also contributed their experience, notably E. S. Cox on various aspects of boiler design, John Lawson in connection with the Caprotti Class 5s, and Bob Watt on his experiences at Perth with the Class 5s fitted with steel fireboxes. I am also indebted to numerous published book sources, in particular *Stanier 4-6-0s of the LMS*, by Rowledge and Reed, which brings together a vast amount of factual information and is a valuable reference source.

The illustrations are a personal selection, aimed as far as possible at showing the wide scope of the day-to-day work of the Stanier 4-6-0s, and its geographical spread, while being satisfying as pictures. They have been chosen from a variety of sources, and inevitably some have appeared before, though hopefully a high proportion will be new to the reader. I am indebted to the Curator of the National Railway Museum, York, and to the Mitchell Library, Glasgow, for permission to reproduce certain photographs and diagrams from their archives. I am grateful to my friend Mr P. B. Whitehouse for making available to me a useful selection of the fine photographs of the late Bishop Eric Treacy, and to Derek Cross and E. D. Bruton as well as to many other contributors from whose valuable repertoires I have been able to take my pick.

A. J. Powell
Dalmeny,
South Queensferry,
West Lothian EH30 9JZ.

1
Introduction

To appreciate fully the part played by the Stanier 4-6-0s following their introduction in 1934, one must really start by looking at the locomotive stock inherited from the constituent companies on amalgamation in 1922/3, and the somewhat unorthodox decisions on new locomotive construction which were implemented during the first 10 years of the new organisation. It would probably be fair to say that only during the final 10 years or so, before nationalisation in 1948, did the LMS have enough motive power of adequate size for the traffic requirements. This was entirely due to the massive locomotive renewal programmes pushed through during W. A. Stanier's tenure as Chief Mechanical Engineer. Production during the reigns of Hughes, Fowler and Lemon had fallen woefully short of these needs. And, sad to say, after nationalisation in 1948 the LM Region, its principal successor, gradually slipped from this position of adequacy to be, perhaps, the one Region amongst all others, most short of locomotives of adequate size.

Table 1

4-6-0 Locomotives inherited by LMS on 1 January 1923

Constituent	Date of Design	Power Class		Sat or Sup	Number	Withdrawn
MR					Nil	
LNWR	1905	3P	'Experiment'	Sat*	105	1925-35
	1906	4F	19in Goods	Sat	170	1931-50
	1911	4P	'Prince'	Sup	245	1933-49
	1913	5P	'Claughton'	Sup	130	1929-49
			Total		650	
LYR	1908	3P	4-cylinder	Sat	5	1925-26
	1921	5P	'Dreadnought'	Sup	29	1934-51
			Total		34	
CR	1902	4P	'55' class	Sat	9	1928-37
	1903	4P	'49' class	Sup	2	1933
	1906	4P	'908' class	Sat	10	1930-35
	1906	4P	'903' class	Sup	4	1927-30
	1906	3F	'918' class	Sat	5	1929-30
	1913	3F	'179' class	Sup	11	1935-46
	1915	4P	'River' (ex-HR)	Sup	6	1939-45
	1916	4P	'60' class	Sup	6	1944-53
	1921	5P	'956' class	Sup	4	1931-35
	1922	3P	'191' class	Sat	8	1939-45
			Total		65	
GSWR	1903	3P	'495' class	Sat	17	1928-33
	1911	3P	'512' class	Sup	2	1933-34
			Total		19	
HR	1894	4F	Jones Goods	Sat	15	1929-40
	1900	3P	'Castle'	Sat	19	1930-46
	1917	4F	Cumming Goods	Sup	8	1946-52
	1919	4P	'Clan'	Sup	8	1943-50
			Total		50	
			Grand Total	(22 classes)	818	

*One rebuild superheated
Note: By 1 January 1932, three classes had been eliminated, and withdrawal of nine further classes had begun.

The LMS at its birth inherited 818 locomotives of 4-6-0 wheel arrangement, or 7.9% of its total fleet of 10,316 locomotives. They comprised no less than 22 different classes, 12 of which consisted of 10 engines or less. The LNWR was by far the largest contributor, with 650 engines; the Midland was the only major constituent to bring none at all. Apart from the LNWR, only the Highland's 4-6-0s formed a substantial proportion of their small stud. Table 1 shows the breakdown of this locomotive stock.

Of the 650 LNWR locomotives, of four classes, 376 were superheated, the 245 'Princes' dating from 1911, the 130 'Claughtons' from 1913, and the odd rebuilt 'Experiment' with four cylinders and Dendy-Marshall valve gear. Under favourable conditions they were able to put up phenomenal performances relative to their size. Unfortunately, they suffered from a number of built-in mechanical weaknesses, particularly in frames and lubrication, which under common user utilisation led to serious unreliability and high unit repair costs; rectification would have needed fundamental and costly modification. Various improvements to the 'Claughtons' in LMS days, even including the upgrading of 20 engines by fitting the $G9\frac{1}{2}S$ boiler, did not tackle these faults. The saturated engines dated from the immediate post-Webb period, and a start on their withdrawal was imminent.

Of the L&YR classes, the five saturated engines were the leftovers from a fundamental rebuilding programme and quickly went to the wall. The superheated 'Dreadnoughts', on the other hand, were almost new engines with an enlightened front end; indeed, building continued until 1925, to a total of 70 locomotives. Some were used competently between Crewe and Carlisle until displaced by the 'Royal Scots' in 1927, when they reverted to their L&Y stamping grounds as a design with no long-term future; withdrawal was in full spate by 1935.

North of the Border, the Caledonian brought into the fold a problem family of 65 robust locomotives of no less than 10 classes, often built as horses-for-courses, and with limited commonality of major components. Half still used saturated steam, and none were more than mediocre for general-purpose work. The big, nearly-new 3-cylinder '956' class could be fairly described as something of a disaster. The 1920s and 1930s saw substantial withdrawals, with only four classes lasting into World War 2. The small G&SWR fleet was completely outclassed and by 1934 had totally disappeared. Only on the Highland was the stock at all matched to the specialised duties required, and this was reflected in their considerable longevity.

So much for the LMS inheritance. From 1923 until the appointment of William Stanier as Chief Mechanical Engineer in January 1932, the direction of locomotive matters, after a hesitant start while newly-appointed officers found their feet in the new organisation and evaluated the various elements of the locomotive fleet and workshop facilities, was a somewhat painful business. There appeared to be few clear and purposefully pursued objectives in relation to the future shape of the locomotive fleet, and what *was* done was bound up with the strengths of the personalities involved, their pre-grouping experience, and a degree of mind-closure to the impact of new circumstances. The inside history of this period has been set down in some detail by E. S. Cox[1], highlighting the influence of the Chief of Motive Power, J. E. Anderson, which was strong to the point of transcending his legitimate responsibilities.

Certain pre-grouping designs, or direct derivatives thereof, were continued in production in limited numbers right up to 1927, either as carryovers from earlier building programmes or by interim selection for particular purposes for which no alternative design was considered to exist. Perhaps the most notable of these was the Horwich 'Dreadnought'. But the 4-6-0 element of the fleet did not generally prosper, and following a relatively good showing in thermal efficiency of the Midland Compounds in dynamometer car trials against LNW and Caledonian designs, the Derby Drawing Office was set to work on adapting selected Midland designs to take over duties from elderly pre-grouping engines throughout the system. From 1924 until 1932, large numbers of very modest-sized locomotives — 4-4-0s and 0-6-0s — were put into service. (Table 2.)

The thoroughly modern Horwich 2-6-0s, sorely needed for express freight and selected passenger work, did not start to arrive until 1926, after some design vacillation, and the first large standard express passenger locomotives, built under near-emergency conditions to meet new operating needs, did not appear until 1927. In the nine years' building activity immediately prior to Stanier's appointment (1923-31 inc), a total of 134 locomotives of 4-6-0 wheel arrangement was added to stock, but of these only the 70 'Royal Scots' and two 'Patriots' represented the top echelon. Even with this construction, the LMS stock of 4-6-0s had increased only from 818 to 856 at the end of 1931 (9.5% of the stock of 9,032 locomotives), and such was the rate of scrapping in the 1930s that by the end of 1934, the first year of mass production of the two Stanier 4-6-0 designs, this figure had actually shrunk to an all-time low of 776, or 9.7% of the rapidly reducing fleet.

Such was the locomotive stock for which Stanier took over responsibility at the beginning of 1932. Coming from Swindon, where a policy of rigid standardisation of modern designs had been pursued for 30 years, the new CME must have looked around him with some little bewilderment, even dismay. In the light of his past experience, he could probably

Table 2

LMS New Locomotive Building, 1923-32

	1923	1924	1925	1926	1927	1928	1929	1930	1931	1932	Total
Pre-Stanier standards											
Cl 6P 4-6-0 'R. Scot'	—	—	—	—	50	—	—	20	—	—	70
Cl 5XP 4-6-0 'Patriot'	—	—	—	—	—	—	—	2*	—	15	17
Cl 4P 4-4-0 Compound	—	40	95	5	50	—	—	—	—	5	195
Cl 2P 4-4-0	—	—	—	—	—	50	19	4	30	35	138
Cl 5MT 2-6-0 Horwich	—	—	—	13	87	8	22	95	10	10	245
Cl 4MT 2-6-4T pb	—	—	—	—	4	21	50	—	—	10	85
Cl 3MT 2-6-2T pb	—	—	—	—	—	—	—	21	39	10	70
Cl 2P 0-4-4T	—	—	—	—	—	—	—	—	—	9	9
2-6-0+0-6-2 Garratt	—	—	—	—	3	—	—	30	—	—	33
Cl 7F 0-8-0	—	—	—	—	—	—	100	3	32	40	175
Cl 4F 0-6-0	—	11	161	132	137	89	—	—	—	—	530
Cl 3F 0-6-0T	—	42	8	128	36	157	36	—	15	—	422
Cl 2F 0-6-0T Dock	—	—	—	—	—	7	3	—	—	—	10
Cl 0F 0-4-0ST	—	—	—	—	—	—	—	—	—	5	5
Total	—	93	264	278	367	332	230	175	126	139	2,004
Non-std new designs											
Cl 5P 4-6-4T Horwich	—	10	—	—	—	—	—	—	—	—	10
Cl 7F 0-8-4T Beames	29	1	—	—	—	—	—	—	—	—	30
Total	29	11	—	—	—	—	—	—	—	—	40
Existing non-std perpetuated											
Cl 5P 4-6-0 Dreadnought	21	16	4	—	—	—	—	—	—	—	41
Cl 4P 4-6-0 'Prince of Wales'	—	1	—	—	—	—	—	—	—	—	1
Cl 4P 4-6-0 CR 14630	—	—	2	18	—	—	—	—	—	—	20
Cl 3P 4-4-2T LT&S	10	—	5	—	10	—	—	10	—	—	35
Cl 2P 0-4-4T CR	—	—	10	—	—	—	—	—	—	—	10
Cl 7F 2-8-0 S&D	—	—	5	—	—	—	—	—	—	—	5
Cl 3F 0-6-2T NS	4	—	—	—	—	—	—	—	—	—	4
Total	35	17	26	18	10	—	—	10	—	—	116
Other Designs											
0-4-0 Sentinel	—	—	—	—	—	—	2	4	—	1	7
Grand Total	64	121	290	296	377	332	232	189	126	140	2,167

*Officially regarded as rebuilds of 'Claughton' locomotives and not normally included in new construction
Total Locomotives built 2,167
of which Cl 6, 5X and 5 372 (17.2%)
of which Cl 5 and above 87 (4.0%)

identify less than 400 locomotives, with another 35 in the current year's building programme, which represented modern design as he understood it. The remainder showed varying degrees of inadequacy, be it in working capacity, availability or reliability, or in the level of maintenance costs, which spelled continuing trouble for years to come.

A glance at the timetable in the early 1930s is needed to put requirements into perspective. The Euston-Birmingham trains were still taking 120 minutes for the 112.9 miles, with a Coventry stop, and loading to about 300 tons. They were often Compound-hauled in the absence of enough 'Patriots'. On the Midland Division, the fastest non-stop working between St Pancras and Leicester, 99.1 miles of difficult but fast road, was 107 minutes, the work shared between 'Patriots', unrebuilt 'Claughtons' and Compounds. The 'Royal Scot' was still allowed $8\frac{1}{4}$ hours for the 401.2 miles from Euston to Glasgow.

On the freight side the only real mixed traffic engines were the Horwich 2-6-0s, very capable machines but inadequate in numbers to cover all the demanding duties within their class. Much express freight work was having to be undertaken by Class 4F 0-6-0s because nothing bigger or better was available. Peter Smith's realistic appraisal of these engines on the Somerset & Dorset line[2] clearly indicates their shortcomings for first-line work.

Conditions were still favourable for the steam locomotive. Good, large coal was readily available at well under £1 per ton — these were the days when depots *built* coal stacks and whitewashed the outsides! — and footplate and maintenance staff of high calibre were there almost for the asking. Furthermore, considerable assistance for investment became available from Government sources to counter the disastrous level of unemployment during the depression.

In this climate, and after changes in senior influential personalities, it was entirely logical that a pressing need should be indentified for the extended building of two new classes of 4-6-0 locomotives. The first, following on from orders for further 'rebuilding' of 'Claughtons' into 'Patriots', was a passenger design, with axleload not exceeding 20 tons,

secondary to the 'Royal Scots' for duties on which the latter could not be used either by route availability limitations or by sheer inadequacy in numbers. In large measure this could be a refined 'Patriot' chassis married to a Stanier/Swindon boiler. Secondly, a mixed traffic locomotive with axleload kept down to about 18 tons was needed, an almost 'go-anywhere' machine with a good turn of speed, and again with a Stanier tapered boiler (though it was not practicable to use a common boiler on both classes). The drawing offices at Derby and Crewe concentrated on the passenger engine, while Crewe and Horwich did much of the work for the mixed traffic locomotive. All were put under heavy pressure by the need for construction to start in the 1934 building programme, and in the three years 1932-34 a total of eight new designs were fully worked up for production.

Until the new designs of 4-6-0 were ready, Stanier continued construction of the 'Patriots' until the spring of 1934 — they were still being described officially as 'Improved Claughtons' in 1933 — albeit with some modification to axleboxes, wheel castings and bogies to bring them into line with his views in these fields. However, in December 1933 the magazine *The Locomotive* recorded that:

'Contracts have been let for the construction of fifty 4-6-0 two-cylinder mixed traffic engines to be built by the Vulcan Foundry Ltd and fifty 4-6-0 three-cylinder passenger engines to be built by the North British Locomotive Co Ltd.'

Though with no hint that the passenger engines were to be anything other than 'Patriots'. Then in March 1934 the magazine reported that at Crewe works:

'Work is now proceeding with a series of fifteen 4-6-0 three-cylinder passenger engines, the last five of which are to have taper boilers.'

Thus did the news emerge of Stanier's 'Jubilees' and Class 5s. The first 'Jubilee', No 5552, was exhibited at Euston Station on 23 April 1934, and a similar showing was arranged for the first Class 5, actually No 5020 built by Vulcan, in September.

Right: Unnamed 'Claughton' No 6012 pulls away from Rugby with a Down express. The engine is in the 1928 livery, and the 12 vehicles are mostly LNWR stock.
Ian Allan Library

Above: Large-boilered Caprotti valve gear 'Claughton' No 5948 *Baltic* coasts into Longwood on a seven-coach Leeds-Manchester Exchange stopping train.   *C. Whitaker*

Left: 'Prince of Wales' No 5671 *Arethusa*, commendably clean, passes Willesden Junction on an Up semi-fast of LNWR stock in November 1931. Note the large lump coal on the tender. *E. R. Wethersett/Real Photos 24041*

Below left: 'Dreadnought' No 10423 working a 10-coach non-corridor Blackpool semi-fast on Lea Road troughs in May 1936. *E. R. Wethersett/Real Photos 24055*

9

Above left: LMS Compound No 1146, built by North British Loco Co, at grips with Beattock bank on a Down special express, assisted in rear. The engine still carries the splash shields for the leading bogie axleboxes. *M. W. Earley*

Left: Ex-CR '60' class No 14652 pounds up Beattock bank on a Down express freight, assisted in rear by an ex-CR 0-4-4T. *M W. Earley*

Below left: Ex-HR 'Clan' No 54767 *Clan Mackinnon* on a cattle train at Kyle of Lochalsh in September 1948, while a 'Cumming Goods' engine in the platform prepares to work the passenger train to Inverness. *C. C. B. Herbert*

Above: With tender overflowing, 'Patriot' No 5518, later to be named *Bradshaw*, reaches the end of Bushey troughs on the 17.50 Euston-Birmingham express in 1935. *Ian Allan Library*

Right: Page from the North British Loco Co's Drawing Office Order Book recording Order L885 for 50 'Jubilees' 'required for summer traffic'. *Mitchell Library, Glasgow*

209

1933

L885   JUBILEE   QP
Nov 2ᵗʰ   5 × P class   HP

London Midland and Scottish Railway Co

Fifty (50) 4-6-0 Superheated Three-cylinder Passenger Engines + Tenders: gauge 4' 8½", cyls (3) 17" × 26", coupled wheels 6'·9' dia, 225 lbs □ working pressure 6 wheel tender; to Rly Co's Drawings + Specification
                                IAP   Nos 24115 - 24139

17.4.34   25 Locos to be built A QP. Words Nos 24140 - 24164

DELIVERY   Required for summer traffic.

            Mr Luckie

D 1897 alteration to smokebox bottom
        + exhaust pipe joints (see LMS Lett 24/8/34)
AS MADES - NONE
SPARES - do
    Nos 5557 - 5606
OUR PROG No 24115 - 24164
Classification Numbers 5 × P
Distinctive Tender Numbers 9004 - 9053

2
The Stanier Marque

Until Stanier's arrival as CME in January 1932, it must be said that detailed locomotive design as managed from Derby showed considerable stagnation. The Midland influence died hard. It continued to show itself in many forms right through to the 'Royal Scots' and 'Patriots', in the chassis, boilers, cab layouts and tenders, even where practice inherited from other constituent railways at grouping was demonstrably superior. To quote two specific examples:

1 The Midland practice of running individual internal steam pipes from the dome to each valve in the cab or elsewhere, and in three cases forward again from there to the front of the boiler continued unabated, the more normal provision of a single feed to a cab manifold, from which the various steam valves were fed externally, being ignored.
2 Coupled axlebox design and lubrication lagged seriously being the times, as did the use of separate axlebox guides instead of hornblocks and the use of non-adjustable spring links.

All too often, when a new design was on the boards and advice was sought, it seemed that the ruling was 'Make it like the "Big Goods" ' — ie the Class 4F 0-6-0 of 1911 vintage.

Into this somewhat introverted world came Stanier, and henceforward life was never quite the same. E. S. Cox has written[3] of the early days of Stanier's CME-ship, recalling :

'... the flat wooden boxes from which he doled out drawings of taper boilers, of smokebox proportions and of other Swindon lore ... the beneficial effect of this influence on LMS design and workshop practice ... the aspects of design to which he unhesitatingly applied GW practice

and those other aspects which he found already developing on sound lines and left alone ...'

Whatever views might be held about the overall concept of GWR locomotive practice, it is undeniable that their detailed design was usually elegant, and improved on things Midland. Not all features from Swindon translated well to LMS conditions, but in general, detailed design practice bucked up enormously under Stanier's influence, and this in turn brought a new attitude of mind to examine and challenge design concepts which stood subsequent CME's in very good stead.

Many of the general features of the Stanier 4-6-0s as they were first built (which applied almost universally to his other classes also), underwent varying degrees of change over the years, either to get over early problems or as part of a process of gradual evolution. Such changes as were initiated during Stanier's CME-ship (up to the end of 1942) will be covered here. Those subsequently made to the Stanier designs under his successors, Fairburn (to a very limited extent) from 1943 to 1945, and the major developments initiated by Ivatt from 1946, will be described in Chapter 5. Various features have been dealt with in some detail elsewhere, and to avoid unnecessary repetition the reader is referred also to the author's previous book[4], and to that by Rowledge and Reed[5].

1 Frames (Fig 1)
The frame plates were by no means generous in thickness, being $1\frac{1}{16}$in on the 'Jubilees' and initially 1in on the Class 5s (up to No 5451)[6]. Furthermore there was little provision of horizontal stays to counter the racking stresses, admittedly difficult on a three-cylinder engine; to provide some

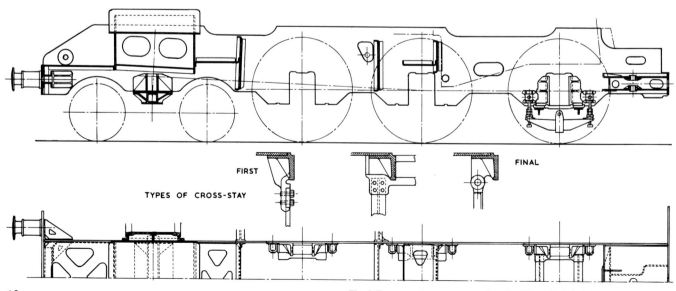

FIRST

FINAL

TYPES OF CROSS-STAY

Fig 1 Frame arrangement of early Class 5 4-6-0s.

additional stiffness, cross-stays were fitted at the bottom of the frame, and detachable, initially at the trailing axle only but later extended to the intermediate axle of the 'Jubilees' (the inside motion prevented their fitting to the leading axle position) and to the leading axle on Class 5s (from No 5275 when new and retrospectively on earlier engines). This left the frames subject to high bending stresses, particularly at the top corners of the horn gaps, where they lacked the stiffening which hornblocks could have provided. The hornstays were not fixed directly to the frames but by studs to the base of the separate axlebox guides, a system difficult to make a good initial fit, and with flexing it led to 'breathing' or just plain looseness in service, adding to the stresses in the frame plate. It could also cause loosening of axlebox guide rivets to the frame, giving another starting point for fractures. Appendix 1 summarises experience, experimental work and repair techniques, particularly on the troublesome Class 5s.

2 Axleboxes

If Stanier is remembered for nothing else (which seems unlikely) his coupled axleboxes will surely be a lasting memorial, for their success had a profound effect on locomotive repairs and availability. Generous sizes, bearing surface continuity and careful attention to lubrication, backed by new workshop techniques in machining and finish which eliminated the need to bed bearings to the journals, came very close to doing away with hot axlebox failures. For instance, during 1939 the 1,000 two-cylinder taper boiler engines then in service produced only 75 hot coupled boxes between them, while the five best classes, totalling 810 locomotives, could produce only 47, or an average of over 16 years per locomotive per coupled box running hot. (The Class 8Fs did not have a single hot box failure in that year.)

The coupled boxes on the 'Jubilees' were on journals 9in dia × 11in long; those on the Class 5s were 8½in dia × 11in long. The cast steel carcase had a pressed-in half-circle brass and slide-in keep containing a generous spring-loaded worsted oil pad. In the first version, oil from the mechanical lubricator was fed to slots at 40° each side of the centre of the crown.[7] This was subsequently altered to a continuous thin white-metal lining on the brass extending over some 140° of arc, with the oil fed to the journal through a series of small holes along the horizontal centreline.[8] This remained the standard arrangement on the 'Jubilees' and the majority of Class 5s, but later batches of the latter were built with the Ivatt arrangement whereby the oil was fed directly into the underkeep to be carried to the journal by the pad alone.

On engines built during Stanier's period of office all these axleboxes had white-metalled faces to the axlebox guides, and as mileage increased, wear and knock developed in the horns, up to .060-.080in on the two-cylinder engines, especially if they were mainly on freight work. Later changes to minimise this wear will be dealt with in Chapter 5.

3 Spring Gear

After the relatively crude Midland practice in laminated spring design and manufacture, Stanier's standards showed considerable refinement. In came silico-manganese ribbed spring plates, machined buckles with wedge retaining plates welded in, more careful control of manufacturing technique, and rocker shoes for the screwed spring links. Some rethinking on numbers and thickness of spring plates proved necessary, however, to increase internal friction and hence hysteresis; on Class 5s, for instance, the original 10-plate

coupled spring, with ⅝in thick leaves, gave way over the years to a 13-plate spring with leaves ½in thick. It was, however, unfortunate that the spring links were in compression, an inherently unstable arrangement which, under the influence of axlebox knock, tended to loosen and shift the buckles.

As in all laminated springs there was a progressive loss of camber, at first rapid and thereafter more gradual until, particularly on the Class 5 trailing axle, the design clearance of 1½in between axlebox top and frame stop was reduced to ⅝in or less; by this time there was violent contact on track irregularities at speed. The adjustment of screwed spring links on the weighbridge was fine when new, but the nuts became immovable in service due to rust and fretting. On Class 5s from No 5462 the compression links were replaced by screwed links in tension with 'mutton-chop' spring link brackets, but this was never built into the 'Jubilees'. While preventing some buckle shifting, the links still siezed up after a period in service and could not be adjusted, and this design was itself superseded in later batches by a simpler one. (See Chapter 5.)

4 Cylinders and Valve Gear

The Class 5s had excellent cylinders with direct steam and exhaust passages,[9] and a clearance volume of 9.5%. Those on the 'Jubilees' had the slightly kinked steam ports of the Fowler LMS designs, but otherwise they left little to be desired. Engines up to No 5664 followed Fowler practice in

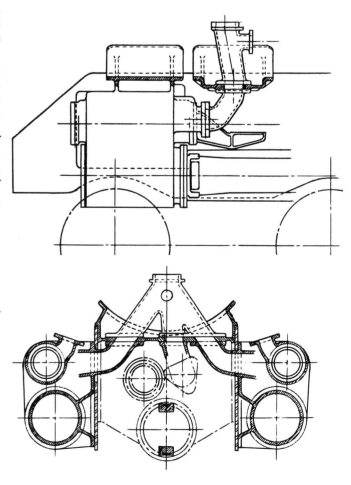

Fig 2 Arrangement of exhaust channels, early 'Jubilee' 4-6-0s.

13

having the exhaust passages from the outside cylinders projecting through the frames, where they joined up with a transversely-mounted three-legged blastpipe casting (Fig 2). This brought problems in the initial alignment of three separate flange faces, in maintaining air-tightness of the smokebox bottom, and in obstructing tube-cleaning. Any cylinder looseness which developed immediately caused leakage and/or fracture, and it is significant that from 1938 the cylinder bolts were increased from $1\frac{1}{4}$in to $1\frac{1}{2}$in to discourage this. The first Class 5s had a slightly different arrangement,[10] in that exhaust channel 'breeches' castings within, but separate from, the smokebox saddle, were flanged to the cylinder face and to a blastpipe base casting set into the smokebox bottom. These not-very-satisfactory designs were superseded in both classess from Nos 5665 and 5225 by what Eric Langridge has called 'slap-on' construction,[11] the outside cylinders being flush-faced and bedded to the frame plate, the exhaust passages being continued within the smokebox saddle section of the inside cylinder casting on the 'Jubilees' and by 'breeches' castings welded integrally into the smokebox saddle on the Class 5s. These arrangements were applied retrospectively for renewals.

Piston valves were 9in dia[12] on the 17in 'Jubilee' cylinders and 10in dia on the $18\frac{1}{2}$in cylinders of the Class 5s. This provided ample port opening at working cutoffs at speed. The Walschaerts valve gear was designed to give fairly long travel with marginally over 75% maximum cutoff. The 'Jubilee' valve characteristics followed those of the 'Royal Scots', in which the lead was progressively increased, first from $\frac{3}{16}$in to $\frac{1}{4}$in and finally to $\frac{5}{16}$in at the expense of the lap, which in consequence became $1\frac{3}{8}$in, with line-and-line exhaust. The 'Jubilees' picked up this process at the halfway stage of $\frac{1}{4}$in lead and $1\frac{7}{16}$in lap, and the lead was increased to $\frac{5}{16}$in following tests in 1937 (see Chapter 4). In the case of the Class 5s, the lap was $1\frac{1}{2}$in, the lead nominally $\frac{1}{4}$in (according to the motion arrangement drawing .2735in on the front ports and .2265in on the back!) and exhaust clearance of $\frac{1}{16}$in was given. Appendices 2 and 3 give further details of the valve events.

The Class 5 valve gear gave events superior to those of the 'Jubilees' in the working range. At 30% cutoff, for example, port openings and releases were similar but compression, despite the $\frac{1}{16}$in exhaust clearance, was some 7% later, as shown in this table:

	'Jubilee'*		Class 5	
Valve travel	3.71in		3.91in	
	F	B	F	B
Port Opening	.41in	.42in	.45in	.45in
Release	73%	72%	72%	70%
Compression	65%	66%	72%	75%

* The figures relate to the gear with $\frac{1}{4}$in lead. The effect of $\frac{5}{16}$in lead (se Chapter 3) would be to increase the port opening to about .47in but the effect on release and compression would be extremely small.

In mechanical design, the Walschaerts valve gear generally incorporated Midland/Fowler features, including the two-piece expansion link bolted together, with two bronze dieblocks, and the four-stud fixing of the return cranks, which had proved highly successful. For a time there was some interest in needle roller bearings for valve gear pins, but their greasing brought difficulties in service and their wear was not superior to that of generous plain bearings. They were abandoned during World War 2 when supply problems arose.

The piston heads started as flat-faced box-section iron castings, screwed directly on to the piston rods with no retaining nut; a bronze spring-loaded slipper was recessed into the bottom of the head to take its weight, and there were three rings. Unfortunately, this simple type of head fixing suffered from early fatigue cracking of the rod at the thread roots, and the design was then changed.

Valve heads were fitted with six rings, $\frac{1}{4}$in wide × $\frac{5}{16}$in deep, prevented from turning in their grooves (and thus trapping the ends in the ports) by brass ring stops screwed into the heads and masking half the groove width.[13] These rings and stops were always somewhat 'tender', needing careful handling during insertion of the valves, and there was some feeling that a four-ring head with beefed-up rings, as applied to one new 'Royal Scot' in 1930, would have been more satisfactory. In the event a different approach to the problem was adopted after World War 2.

5 Cylinder Lubrication (Fig 3)

The cylinders were lubricated by a 'Silvertown' mechanical lubricator.[14] This gave atomised feeds to an annular ring round each valve chest liner, and 'solid' feeds to top and bottom centre of the cylinder barrel, and to the piston rod gland and rear valve spindle bushing. This system gave good wear levels, though this was higher on Class 5s than on 'Jubilees'. As an example, the cylinder records of 'Jubilee' No 45593 show that between 1948 and 1962 (she was withdrawn in 1967) the outside cylinders were each rebored four times at works overhauls, while the middle cylinder was rebored only once; in that time the maximum wear plus reboring loss was only .237in L, .154in M and .265in R on diameter.

Drivers were instructed to coast on 45-55% cutoff, but in practice almost all dropped the engine into full gear when coasting, despite then having to wind the gear back again. This aggravated suction down the blastpipe. Depending on the depot and the work on which employed, the Class 5 valves and ports could get quite dirty, due to suction of char down the blastpipe when coasting, but the 'Jubilees' kept extremely clean, due to the balanced suction, and it was established that they could run 40-48,000 miles before opening up for valve and piston examination without detriment.

6 Wheels and Balancing

By the time Stanier took over, the LMS had established design criteria and workshop machining practices for wheels and tyres which virtually eliminated tyre fractures, and with little fundamental change these features — a stiffer wheel rim section, tyre fastening by Gibson ring, and fine-finish machining of the tyre bore — were continued. However, on the 'Jubilees' some ex-'Claughton' bogie wheel sets continued in use, and these retained earlier forms of fastening.

Stanier brought with him the practice of built-up balance weights in coupled wheels, plates riveted over the spokes being selectively filled with a molten lead/antimony mixture to give smooth running on the high-speed balancing machine with equivalent weights on the crankpins. This was a distinct improvement, both in accuracy and in foundry practice, over balance weights cast solid in the wheels of earlier engines.

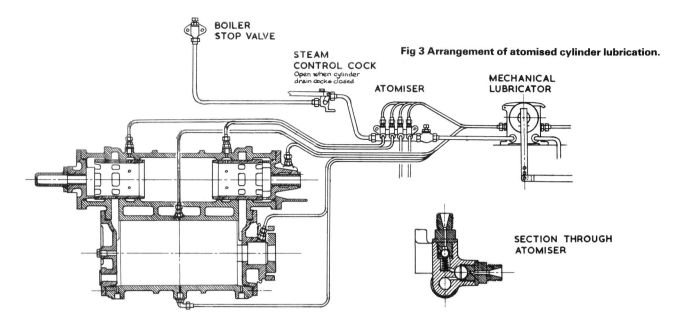

BOILER STOP VALVE

STEAM CONTROL COCK
Open when cylinder drain cocks closed

ATOMISER

MECHANICAL LUBRICATOR

Fig 3 Arrangement of atomised cylinder lubrication.

SECTION THROUGH ATOMISER

As was general at the time, both 'Jubilees' and early Class 5s were built with 66% of the reciprocating masses balanced, in all cases equally divided between coupled wheels to keep down the hammerblow per wheel.

In the 227 Armstrong Whitworth Class 5s of 1936/7 this proportion was reduced to 55%, and in the 1938 construction a further reduction was made to 50%. (See Appendix 4.)

The very high speeds of which the Class 5s proved capable led to some tests in 1939 involving slipping on greased rail at about 8rps, and Appendix 4 outlines the results. As a result, 50% reciprocating balance was adopted for future Class 5 construction, though no retrospective re-balancing was done. Surprisingly, there was a reversion later to 66% on new construction.

7 Bogies

It has been said[15] that, because design priorities in the drawing office did not produce drawings for a new 6ft 6in wheelbase side-bolster bogie in time, the initial orders on Crewe for 53 'Jubilees' were turned out with a 6ft 3in wheelbase bogie common to the 'Patriots'. Nevertheless, it proved possible to incorporate the new 6ft 6in bogie in the North British order for 50 'Jubilees' (which were appearing at the same time as the first Crewe orders) and in the three-cylinder 2-6-4 tank engines built at Derby, several of which were in service before Crewe's first 4-6-0. The fact is that, as an economy measure, the bogie frames and axlebox guides used at Crewe on these 53 engines were ex-'Claughton' items, extended by welding to suit new front and rear plate cross-stays instead of the standard bar stays; the scrapping rate of the 'Claughtons' was consistent with their availability. These early 'Jubilee' bogies were never rebuilt with side bolsters and carried the load through the pivot centres.

All other 'Jubilees', and all Class 5s, carried the standard 6ft 6in bogie in which the weight was transferred through side bolsters with spherical mating surfaces, the male components being bolted below the frame cross-stay while the flat base of the female components (familiarly known as the 'spittoon') was fitted with a friction pad of 'Ferobestos' or similar material which slid on brass liners on the bogie centre casting. The bogie frames were fairly free to float independently of the axles and springs, and could be rocked easily up and down for about 1½in under load, using a pinch-bar. Side control was by helical springs fore and aft of the bogie centre casting, having a 'crack-off' loading of 1.9 tons

before movement began. The riding of all engines with this bogie was excellent.

8 Sanding Apparatus

Stanier did not adopt from the outset the well-tried Midland steam sanding gear, preferring dry gravity sanding à la Swindon, mechanically controlled. He was prevailed upon by the Signal Engineer to supplement this with a water de-sanding device behind the coupled wheels in each direction of travel, to wash sand off the rail head to prevent interference with track circuits. By 1936 it was accepted that this apparatus was difficult to maintain effectively, and on new construction a changeover was made to traditional steam sanding, early engines being modified retrospectively.

9 Firebox

The heart of the Stanier boiler was the Belpaire firebox, and here lay the greatest improvement over the very square Midland variety. The outer and inner wrapper plates were in flowing curves. On the straight throatplate boilers the wrapper stays were of copper except in the side breaking zones, and on the crown, where steel stays, nutted on the inside to prevent erosion by the fire, were used (following the practice begun with the 'Royal Scots'). In the sloping throatplate boilers the copper stays were replaced by more slender monel metal, also nutted on the inside. This overall layout proved most satisfactory; stay leakage was negligible, breakage was rare, and the inner copper firebox, except for the tubeplate and perhaps a new half-side welded in because of cinder-cutting on the ogee bend, usually lasted the life of the engines. A minor nuisance was a certain build-up of birds nesting on the stay nuts, which required brushing off at washouts. The superheater flues were screwed into the copper tubeplate against a 45° seating and the ends beaded over, while the small tubes were expanded and rolled over in the normal way.

In the straight throatplate boilers of both '3A' and '3B' types, the grates had a very pronounced hump when built, the front portion sloping down at about 3.2:1 and the back section being level. In the '3A' 'Jubilee' boiler this hump was exactly in the centre of the grate, some 5ft from the firehole door, and this made it tricky to fire accurately to the front half of the grate without leaving the middle too thin; undoubtedly some of the early steaming troubles could be laid at this door. Before long, an alteration to the firebar

15

bearers eased the front slope. In the case of the '3B' Class 5 boilers the hump was rather nearer the door, and thus did not mask the front slope to the same extent. In the sloping throatplate boilers the humps were moderated, the level portion being restricted to one third of the grate and the slope of the remainder eased to about 4.3:1, making it much easier to place coal over a thicker fire inside the door.

One of the less satisfactory features of LMS engines in general was the brick arch design. This comprised heavy side bricks resting on steel arch bars, with large archbricks in pairs resting on them. Seven or eight pairs constituted the arch proper. These large bricks were subject to spalling, due to some lack of homogeneity and penetration by fused ash, and when this occurred they were liable to drop the main arch bricks into the fire. Arch life was sometimes only a fortnight or even less. There was some success in the 1950s and 1960s with monolithic arches cast in situ from refractory concrete on Class 5s, though life was somewhat variable.

10 Tube Layouts and Superheaters

Stanier initially disposed the main body of small tubes in vertical rows, as on the other railways, instead of adopting the Midland practice of horizontal rows. In theory, this arrangement gave a freer upward circulation of heated water, but the effect in practice seemed negligible, and with higher superheat came a reversion to horizontal rows, but with reduced tubeplate bridges.

New standards were also introduced in the superheater elements. The normal Superheater Co's return loop elements were not used; instead, the downcomer pipes divided just outside the smokebox tubeplate, forming two parallel circuits for the steam. These bifurcated elements (in the case of the 'Duchesses' they were trifurcated) were standard until World War 2, when manufacturing restrictions forced the adoption of the return loop type, and this was not changed again. As will be seen in Chapter 4, the effect on steam temperatures was small, but marginally in favour of the return loop type.

The whole question of tube proportions, superheat, etc will be discussed in the next chapter.

11 Topfeed (Fig 4)

The standard topfeed clackboxes were mounted, with three-stud flanges and spherical joint rings, on a steel manhole cover, and contained reversible clack valves working in a cage. The injector delivery pipe was secured to the bottom of the box by a four-stud flange with spherical joint ring. The feed water was deflected into shallow zinc trays, arranged pannier-fashion each side of the main steam pipe, overflowing thence into the barrel. This GWR system was expensive to install, and bitterly disliked by the Motive Power Department, which was expected to clear it of deposits as a regular examination. It was therefore abandoned during World War 2 in favour of a simple internal deflector plate guiding the water down the barrel sides.

There was very little trouble with sticking clacks, except in districts with very hard water. There was, however, plenty of trouble from leakage at the flange joints, particularly under vibration conditions on the two-cylinder engines, and a multitude of official experiments was made, using alternative forms of joint and clipping of the delivery pipe. From these, 'Metaflex' joints, a thick combination asbestos/stainless steel sandwich packing, emerged as satisfactory, and was adopted latterly. This overall design of topfeed was replaced on new construction during the Fairburn regime (Chapter 5).

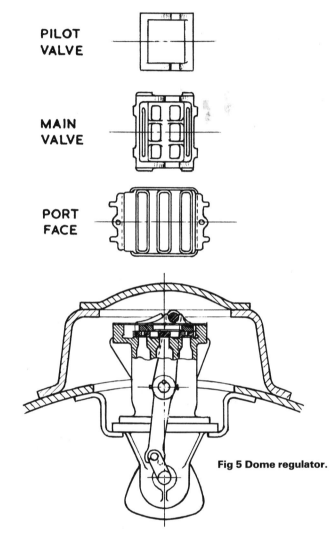

Fig 5 Dome regulator.

12 Regulators

Domeless boilers had the regulator valves in a sizeable chamber in the superheater header; a small sight-feed lubricator in the cab was necessary to lubricate the valves because of the high working temperature. It was not a good arrangement, lacking sensitivity for the driver at the other end of a 24ft long operating rod; accessibility for maintenance was poor, and the header castings were prone to cracking. Stanier therefore reverted to a dome regulator (Fig 5), disposed horizontally instead of in the more usual vertical position — making it more accessible — with main and pilot valves giving differential action on opening and closing.[16] Due to its imbalance the regulator handle was fitted with a

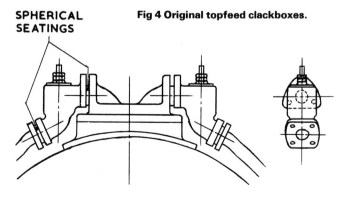

SPHERICAL SEATINGS

Fig 4 Original topfeed clackboxes.

spring-loaded catch which engaged on detents on the stuffing box quadrant in the 'full open' and 'breath of steam' positions, but this was only moderately successful and did not, of course, provide for intermediate positions. Many drivers, therefore, carried small wooden wedges to insert against the quadrant stop to prevent the regulator closing involuntarily; alternatively, a suitable piece of coal would be used. The dome regulators needed no lubricator, and the cracked header syndrome largely disappeared.

13 Smokeboxes
The circular smokebox used on all Stanier engines, sitting on a cast or (usually) fabricated saddle, virtually ended the problems inherent in the D-section smokeboxes of Fowler days, which were well-nigh impossible to keep airtight with the racking of the frames at high mileages. The deep-dished door and door ring were machined on the inclined mating faces to give a metal-to-metal joint. Provided that disposal crews brushed this joint clear of char before closing the door, it remained airtight; without this elementary precaution, distortion and thus leakage *could* take place, but burnt doors on Stanier engines were rare sights.

Originally, both 'Jubilees' and Class 5s were fitted with deflector plates in the smokebox, intended mainly to prevent spark emission, but also to balance the draught across the tubeplate. These plates interfered with daily tube cleaning at depots, however, and their removal and replacement was a very unpleasant job; they also took some blame for poor steaming. So they were soon relegated to dumps in the darkest corners of sheds until being officially discarded.

14 Firedoors
The LMS was always a sliding firedoor railway. With the laudable aim of easing the fireman's work, Stanier engines started off with fairly thin doors, hung on rollers from a top rail, but when running the movement of the engine tended to close the doors, for they were very free running. This was not too popular with firemen, who would swing the shovel only to find the doors closing in front of it! Drivers got involved in holding them open, and many were the attempts to find something to wedge on the bottom guide rail to keep them so. A changeover to more conventional sliding doors was later made retrospective, using a much deeper section casting to admit more secondary air. A smaller hinged flap plate inside the doors was also adopted, over which the back half of the grate could be fired while minimising admission of cold air.

Mention must be made of the 'smoke plate' or deflector plate in the upper half of the firehole to prevent cold air taking a short cut to the tubeplate. The small 'ears' on it, together with the firehole protector casting on which it sat, determined its angle of repose. But invariably it drooped and interfered with firing towards the front of the grate; to overcome this, firemen often inserted a large bolt — chair screws were popular and readily available — over the centre of the plate to cock it up somewhat. Woe betide the fireman who was found by an inspector to have done this! All went well so long as the bolt remained where it should, but if it was going to move there was only one way in which it could do so — back towards the doors. If this happened while the doors were shut, it would jam them in that position, and then many an anxious minute was spent when firing came to an involuntary halt until brute force could be bought to bear. Which was one reason why inspectors tried to stop the practice!

15 Brakes
Engine and tender had vacuum-controlled steam brakes in accordance with standard LMS practice, and following Fowler precedent both 'Jubilees' and Class 5s started life with crosshead-operated vacuum pumps in addition to large and small ejectors, to save steam while running. Steam valves for both ejectors were contained within the 'Dreadnought' brake valve, with pull-down handle. But by 1937 crosshead pumps were out of favour, due mainly to their maintenance needs, and were removed at works repairs. The 'Dreadnought' valves also gave way to the standard Midland combined vacuum/steam brake valve (a far-from-satisfactory device which was not properly graduable on the steam brake side) and separate ejector steam valves above it.

Some minor refinements were introduced into the brake rigging to present the single brake blocks correctly to the 1 in 20 tyre coning, and this prevented much flanging of the blocks. At first the rigging was not equalised, and this feature did not appear until after Stanier's departure.

16 Cabs
The side-window Stanier cab offered good weather protection, though when teamed up with the narrow Fowler 3,500 gallon tender it could be draughty. The wooden tip-up seats were sometimes criticised, but they were robust, profiled (those made by the works, anyway!) to give reasonable comfort, and easily put out of the way when not required. The controls were all well placed to hand, except for the blower valve above the firehole door (which, while fine for the fireman when firing, was badly placed for either man while seated, in case of a blow-back), and the duplicated whistle handles under the cab roof which were just out of reach when sitting down.

The 4-6-0s were originally fitted with sandguns above the firehole doors, which could be operated to draw sand from a small sandbox in the cab and blow it over the firebox tubeplate to keep it, and the tubes, clean of deposits. In practice, it was little used and was removed during the 1940's.

Perhaps the least satisfactory features in service were:

1 The damper controls.
  All 'Jubilees' and early Class 5s were built with quadrant levers in the floor, with crude throwover catches which often needed supplementing with wedges, etc, to make the levers stay put. Some engines later got the standard 'walking stick' pull-up handles in lieu, but the spring catches on these were no more reliable, and the handles frequently needed string, spanners, bricks and other assorted assistance to hold them open!

2 The provision for fireirons.
  In all cases this involved turning hot fireirons after use through 180° to stow them, either in the fireiron tunnel on Stanier tenders — which was awkward enough — or in a rough-and-ready rack *on top of the coal* on the Fowler tenders. These fireirons were longer than the width of the cab, making it a downright dangerous manoeuvre.[17] On his 2-6-0s Ivatt put the fireiron tunnels on the fireman's side engine footframing, but this was never extended to new Class 5 construction.

17 Preparation and Disposal
Both classes were covered by the standard preparation allowance of 60 minutes for engines with a heating surface in

excess of 1,500sq ft, surely one of the most illogical agreements ever made with the trade unions. Any three-cylinder engine is necessarily a longer and less pleasant job to prepare than a machine with two outside cylinders. The inside cylinder of the 'Jubilees' was set forward over the leading bogie axle, no access hole could be cut in the frames behind it, and in order to get at the inside crosshead, slidebars and little end there was no option but for the driver (or more usually the fireman, being younger!) to climb up from the pit and inject himself into the maze formed by the motion plate, bogie centre, bogie trailing axle and cross-stay, and leading brake crossbeam, preferably with the inside crank behind bottom centre. Needless to say, it was just about the filthiest workplace imaginable, worthy of a special pair of overalls for this alone. Access from above was almost nil. By contrast, the Class 5s were often prepared without even going into the pit.

On disposal, the 'Jubilees' were always devoid of the later labour-saving fittings, such as rocking grates, hopper ashpans and self-cleaning smokeboxes,[18] and so were about two-thirds of the Class 5s. So cleaning the fire was a job for strong muscles and determination, either paddling clinker out via the firehole and over the side of the footplate — if the fire was in not too bad shape — or by lifting several firebars with long-handled tongs and pushing the dirty fire down into the ashpan.[19] The ashpan had to be raked by hand from the pit through both front and back damper openings because of the hump over the trailing axle. The smokebox needed cleaning after every trip; indeed, with the early 'Jubilee' boilers with $2\frac{1}{8}$in tubes, I have seen engines come on to Derby shed from St Pancras with char piled up well above the blastpipe cap. (And there are still enthusiasts — bystanders, not the enginemen who did it every day — who long for the return of coal-fired steam!)

The Stanier Look

Above: 'Jubilee' No 5573, brand new, poses outside North British Loco Co's Hyde Park Works, Glasgow in September 1934. She has the domeless straight-throatplate boiler and 4,000gal tender. Note the crosshead-driven vacuum pump and dry sanding with water de-sanding jets.
Mitchell Library, Glasgow

Right: Twenty-six years later, Crewe-built 'Jubilee' No 45675 *Hardy* on Willesden shed shows the same general outline. Built with domed sloping-throatplate boiler, she shows few external changes; the vacuum pump has long gone, though the crosshead still bears the signs of the arm mounting; the Smith-Stone speedometer generator has appeared on the trailing crankpin, steam sanding is fitted, and the vacuum trainpipe connection from the ejectors is now a hose rather than a copper pipe. *C. P. Boocock*

Above: Seen from behind, preserved 'Jubilee' No 5593 *Kolhapur*, a North British product, emphasises the lines of her taper boiler and looks every bit a racehorse. This engine is, at the time of writing, undergoing an extensive overhaul at the Birmingham Railway Museum, Tyseley.
P. B. Whitehouse

Below left: Preserved Class 5 No 5025, built by Vulcan Foundry in August 1934, and in almost original external condition, stands at Inverness in October 1982, being watered before working a Toyota charter special to Kyle of Lochalsh. She still

carries a domeless straight-throatplate boiler, and apart from the AWS inductor under the front buffer beam and the reservoir in front of the cab, faithfully portrays the 1930s look.
C. P. Boocock

Below right: An Armstrong-Whitworth-built Class 5, No 45239, fresh from General Repair at Crewe in March 1964, typifies the class in BR days. As always she carries a domed sloping-throatplate boiler. The vacuum pump has disappeared, Smith-Stone speedometer fitted, and smokebox lamp bracket moved.   *G. H. Wheeler*

Stanier Features

Above: 'Jubilees' under erection at North British Loco Co's Hyde Park Works in 1934. The 'Alfol' boiler insulation is being fitted, through the lower firebox sides, inaccessible when in the frames, are already 'plastered' with magnesite insulation. The topfeed clackboxes, safety valves and regulator rod are fitted, but backplate fittings remain to be added.
Mitchell Library, Glasgow

Centre right: Spare boilers outside Crewe Works, 1963. The second firebox is that of a '3A' straight-throatplate boiler, and shows the slender steel stays in the breaking zone, surrounded by riveted copper stays. The boiler steadying bracket shows below the firehole. On the ground below is one of the newer topfeed mountings.
R. Wildsmith

Below right: Exhaust channels and blastpipe base as used on early Class 5s
Crown Copyright National Railway Museum York

Left: Cab view of 'Jubilee' No 5573 when new. The heat-proof handles on steam valves were replaced quickly by handwheels with tails, or spanner squares. The original 'Dreadnought' brake valve is evident, as is the regulator sight-feed lubricator above it to the right. The fitting on the right of the firebox is the combined blowdown/ desanding valve, which was subsequently changed. Note that at this stage no sandgun was fitted.
Mitchell Library, Glasgow

Below: Class 5 No 5125 is hauled from Armstrong-Whitworth's Newcastle works to Crewe for commissioning in May 1935. This shows the standard preparations for delivery 'dead'. Coupling and connecting rods were carried in the bunker, and the crossheads held by wood lashed to the bottom slidebar. The eccentric rods remained, to operate the axlebox mechanical lubricator.
Ian Allan Library

Preparation and Disposal

Above: Oiling the motion of a Class 5, Westerleigh Yard. This shows how almost all the oil-can preparation could be done from ground level without need of a pit.   *G. F. Heiron*

Above right: 'Jubilee' No 45623 gets the rear section of the ashpan raked from the pit side at Edge Hill, 1953. The front section could only be done from the ashpit.   *R. Hewitt*

Below: Smokebox char is raked from the smokebox of No 45627 at Kentish Town after working an Up express, 1951. *A. B. Thornton*

Right: In the gloom of Leeds Holbeck shed, a cold 'Jubilee' gets her tubes swept through, using cotton waste on a long rod. *Ian Allan Library*

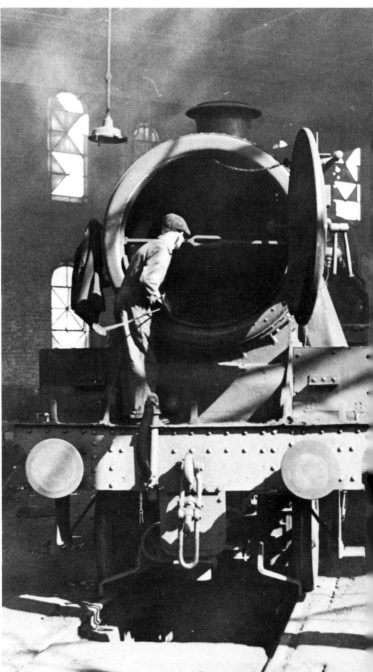

3
Getting the Boilers Right

There can be little doubt that the 'Jubilees' and Class 5s were subjected to more official testing than any other group of locomotives in Britain. In the case of the 'Jubilees', intensive testing was essential in conjunction with boiler and draughting modifications to ensure that the locomotives could do the job for which they had been built. By contrast, the Class 5s had few problems in settling down as effective traffic machines, and testing was largely devoted to evaluation of new developments and of features which could be of wider significance, using them as convenient guinea-pigs.

So the development process for these engines tends to fall naturally into three phases, namely:

a) Dynamometer car testing of the original designs, and modifications to them, to produce a satisfactory standard of performance.

This phase covered the period from September 1934 to mid-1937, and will constitute the theme of this chapter.

b) Dynamometer car testing, usually on special trains, to prove revised timings and loadings for timetable accelerations.

This work was almost confined to 1937, and will be covered in Chapter 4 along with day-to-day running until the end of World War 2.

c) Testing, usually using more sophisticated equipment under controlled conditions, of new or modified features, or to establish output characteristics for timetabling purposes.

This phase stretched from 1948 until the further development of steam traction ceased in Britain in the late 1950s, and will in the main be reviewed in Chapter 6.

A very little of the testing work did not naturally fall within this classification, and will be included as thought most appropriate.

This chapter will, therefore, concentrate within this overall framework on the efforts to make the 'Jubilees' steam satisfactorily, together with work on the Class 5s to improve their efficiency, since their ability to steam was hardly in doubt. For the most part, these efforts were so intimately concerned with changes in boiler proportions and draughting design that it seems approriate to interlock the two into a single account.

First, some comments on the proportions of boilers generally. Now hindsight is a most useful attribute which enables us to argue knowledgeably about tube proportions and gas flow. But it must be recognised that these aspects of boiler design were by no means so well documented in 1934

as they are now. True, R. P. Wagner had read a paper to the Institution of Locomotive Engineers in 1929[20] which critically examined tube proportions in a Deutsche Reichsbahn context, and which received some sceptical acknowledgement from, amongst others, Sir Henry Fowler. There was also some sound guidance on the subject tucked away in Lawford Fry's book[21] based entirely on US practice, but few locomotive engineers in Britain seemed to have read it and taken it to their bosoms. The fundamental ratios which, if well chosen, could go far to assuring the success of a boiler did not become very consciously accepted until the reading of a paper by Loubser and Cox[22] to the Institution of Locomotive Engineers in 1938, part of which was devoted to the tribulations of the 'Jubilee' boilers. By the same token, there was little published information about blastpipe/chimney proportions which was readily applicable, particularly to three-cylinder engines, and these were largely settled by a mixture of past experience and trial and error.

It was perhaps inevitable that in this climate with a new design philosophy applied rapidly on a large scale, changes in tube layout and draughting would be found necessary. In the case of the 'Jubilees' these changes were very complex, the boilers running through no less than 17 variations, not many of which survived; the relevant details and ratios are contained in Table 3. The corresponding details for the Class 5s were simpler, comprising only 10 variations, shown in Table 4. Throughout the remainder of this book, reference to the boiler of any engine involved in test running will be by the relevant line number in these tables.

In studying Tables 3 and 4, four things should be particularly borne in mind. Firstly, as a general principal, the proportion of the total free gas area provided by the superheater flues (col 10) gives a rough yardstick to the degree of superheat in the steam. Secondly, the ratio of cross-sectional area of a small tube to its gas swept surface area — the A/S ratio of column 6 — was crucial to success. The generally accepted otimum value for this ratio on medium-sized and large boilers is 1/400. Pre-Stanier Derby designs, decided very much by rule of thumb, varied between 1/342 (Garratts) and 1/409 (Class 7F 0-8-0s). A tendency began in 1926, in modifying the original LNWR 'Claughton' boilers, to go for larger tubes than hitherto,[23] and this continued with the $2\frac{1}{8}$in tubes, 14ft 0in between tubeplates, in the G9½S boiler designed for the 'Claughton' rebuilds and 'Patriots', as compared with 2in dia, 14ft 6in between tubeplates on the parallel-boilered 'Royal Scots', which latter had a perfect ratio of 1/399. This Derby fondness for over-large small tubes shines through the early years of the 'Jubilee' saga, causing steaming problems, and the concept was not finally killed off until 1936. Fortunately this aberration was not built into the Class 5s, except for the odd engine for test purposes.

Table 3
'Jubilee' class 4-6-0s: Class '3A' taper boilers

Throatplate Length between Tubeplates / Grate Area	Line No	Superheater		Small Tubes		Free Gas Areas (sq ft)			Superheater as % of Total	Free Gas Area as % of Grate Area	Remarks
		Flues 5⅛in × 7swg	Elements dia 11swg	(11swg) dia	A/S ratio	Superheater	Small Tubes	Total			
Cols 1	2	3	4	5	6	7	8	9	10	11	12
Straight Throatplate 14ft 3in 29.5sq ft	1	14	1⅜in bifurc	160 2in	1/389	1.16	2.73	3.89	29.8	13.2	Nos 5552-5641, 5647-5664 as built.
	2	21	1⅛in	130 2in	1/389	2.03	2.22	4.25	47.8	14.4	Nos 5642-5646 as built.
	3	14	1⅜in bifurc	26 2in / 134 2⅛in	1/389 / 1/364	1.16	3.06	4.22	27.5	14.3	Nos 5556, 5558 retubed at first SR for tests Feb-May 1935
	4	21	1⅛in	138 2⅛in	1/364	2.03	2.70	4.73	42.9	16.0	No 5645 as retubed for tests April 1935
	5	21	1⅛in	38 2in / 92 2⅛in	1/389 / 1/364	2.03	2.45	4.48	45.3	15.2	No 5645 as retubed for tests May/June 1935
	6	21	1¼in	168 2in	1/389	1.89	2.87	4.76	39.7	16.1	No 5554 as retubed 1935
	7	14	1⅜in bifurc	158 2in	1/389	1.16	2.70	3.86	30.1	13.2	Line 1 boilers modified at first GR to improve washout provision
	8	21	1⅛in	128 2in	1/389	2.03	2.19	4.22	48.1	14.4	Line 2 boilers modified at first GR to improve washout provision
	9	24	1¼in return loop	159 1⅞in	1/419	2.16	2.34	4.50	48.0	15.3	All straight throatplate boilers when tubeplates renewed prewar.
	10	24	1⅜in	159 1⅞in	1/419	1.99	2.34	4.33	46.0	14.7	When fitted with postwar elements
Sloping Throatplate 13ft 2⅞in 31.0sq ft	11	21	1⅛in	168 1⅞in	1/390	2.03	2.47	4.50	45.1	14.5	No 5665 as built
	12	21	1⅛in	138	1/338	2.03	2.70	4.73	42.9	15.3	Nos 5666-5676, 5678-5694 as built
	13	28	1⅛in	105 2⅛in	1/338	2.71	2.05	4.76	56.9	15.4	No 5677 as built
	14	21	1¼in	138 2⅛in	1/338	1.89	2.70	4.59	41.2	14.8	Nos 5695-5701 as built
	15	24	1¼in	159 1⅞in	1/390	2.16	2.34	4.50	48.0	14.5	Nos 5702-5730, 5732-5742 as built, and sloping throatplate boilers when tubeplates renewed
	16	24	1in trifurc	159 1⅞in	1/390	2.32	2.34	4.66	49.8	15.0	No 5731 as built
	17	24	1⅜in	159 1⅞in	1/390	1.99	2.34	4.33	46.0	14.0	When fitted with postwar elements

Thirdly, and arising from the second point, any wide divergence between the A/S ratios of superheater flues and small tubes could seriously unbalance the gas flow through the tube bank, adversely affecting superheat temperatures.

Finally, the ratio of total free gas area to grate area (col 11) is decisive in determining the ultimate steaming capacity of the boiler — always subject to satisfactory resolution of the other three factors. The ideal is generally accepted as 15-16%; the original layout on the 'Jubilees' was seriously deficient at only 13.2%. On the Class 5s, by contrast, the smaller grate area meant that superheaters of 21 and more elements brought the proportion into the ideal range.

It must be said that the increase in grate area in the sloping throat-plate boilers had little perceptible effect on performance. Indeed, the majority of Midland Division 'Jubilees', performing some of the hardest work diagrammed to these engines anywhere on the LMS and LM Region, were overwhelmingly fitted with straight throatplate boilers, and this remained the position for over 20 years.

Construction

The first batch of 'Jubilees', Nos 5552-5556, were turned out from Crewe in May and June 1934, with line 1 boilers (Table 3) having 14 elements giving low superheat. A jumper blastpipe with 5⅛in dia cap 3in below boiler centreline (very high for a modern engine) exhausted into a chimney tapered at 1 in 7. North British Locomotive Co started producing their order for 50 engines (Nos 5557-5606) in June 1934, also with line 1 boilers, and Crewe immediately followed their first batch with a second order for 48, also mainly with line 1 boilers. These were all in service by April 1935, after which there was a pause before further construction started.

In the case of the Class 5s, and very unusually for the LMS, the first engine, No 5020, came from the Newton-le-Willows works of Vulcan Foundry early in August 1934; the first engine built in railway works, at Crewe, did not appear until six months later as No 5000, by which time Vulcan had completed their initial order for 50 engines and were starting to deliver their second order for 50 (Nos 5075-5124). Such was the demand for the new engines, to replace scrapped pre-

Table 4
Class 5MT 4-6-0s: Class '3B' taper boilers

Throatplate Length between Tubeplates Grate Area	Line No	Superheater		Small Tubes		Free Gas Area (sq ft)			Superheater as % of Total	Free Gas Area as % of Grate Area	Remarks
		Flues 5⅛in dia × 7swg	Elements dia 11swg	(11swg) dia	A/S ratio	Superheater	Small Tubes	Total			
Cols 1	2	3	4	5	6	7	8	9	10	11	12
Straight Throatplate 14ft 3in 27.8sq ft	1	14	1⅜in bifurc	160 2in	1/389	1.16	2.73	3.89	29.8	14.0	Nos 5000-5006, 5020-5069 as built
	2	21	1¼in bifurc	138 2in	1/389	1.89	2.35	4.24	44.6	15.3	Nos 5007-5019, 5070-5104, 5125-5174 as built
	3	21	1¼in bifurc	136 2in	1/389	1.89	2.32	4.21	44.9	15.1	Nos 5105-5124, 5175-5224 as built, to improve washout provision
	4	21	1⅛in bifurc	136 2⅛in	1/364	2.03	2.66	4.69	43.3	16.9	No 5079 as retubed for tests April 1935.
	5	21	1⅛in bifurc	136 2in	1/389	2.03	2.32	4.35	46.7	15.6	No 5159 as tested January 1937. No 45218 as tested at Rugby 1950.
	6	24	1¼in	159 1⅞in	1/419	2.16	2.34	4.50	48.0	16.2	All straight throatplate boilers when tubeplates renewed
	7	24	1⅜in return loop	159 1⅞in	1/419	1.99	2.34	4.33	46.0	15.6	When fitted with postwar elements
Sloping Throatplate 13ft 2⅞in 28.65sq ft	8	24	1¼in bifurc	159 1⅞in	1/390	2.16	2.34	4.50	48.0	14.5	Nos 5225-5451 as built
	9	28	1¼in	151 1⅞in	1/390	2.52	2.22	4.74	53.2	16.2	Nos 5452-5471, 4921-4999, 44698-44717, 44738-44799 as built
	10	28	1⅜in	151 1⅞in	1/390	2.32	2.22	4.54	51.1	15.8	Nos 5472-5499, 4800-4920, 44718-44737, 44658-44697 as built. Line 9 boilers fitted with postwar elements

grouping designs and to take over from less competent classes, that in 17 months from their first appearance until December 1935 no less than 225 Class 5s were built. All had the straight throatplate boiler, although changes had already begun. As Crewe completed its first 20 engines, and followed on with the odd five (Nos 5070-5074), Armstrong Whitworth on Tyneside embarked on delivery of 100 engines (Nos 5125-5224).

Tests in 1934

The new 'Jubilees' had not been very long in traffic before their steaming capabilities were being adversely compared by enginemen with the 'Patriots', which themselves were no paragons when pushed. Yet they were given four months to settle down before any tests were started. In contrast, the first Class 5 had barely been run in before she was put through her paces with the Dynamometer car in September 1934 on passenger trains between Crewe and Euston, on 'Special Limit' timings which allowed a Class 5 370 tons. While the Up train was kept within this limit the Down train, normally a 'Royal Scot' turn, loaded successively to 410, 415 and finally 468 tons. Grimethorpe Grade 1 coal was burnt. The engine had, of course, her original line 1 boiler (Table 4). The interim report on the tests (no final copy has been traced) was enthusiastic:

'The engine maintained the booked timing without difficulty and gained time with the heaviest load hauled (468 tons, 14.40 ex-Euston) taking this train without the banking engine out of Euston.'

17-20% cutoff with full regulator was sufficient for general running, with 25% on the banks, and even with 468 tons, 20-25% was enough generally, with 25-30% on the banks. The steaming was 'uniform and adequate throughout', which might be taken to imply something not quite good enough for everyday conditions. Nevertheless, the general performance was described as 'very satisfactory'.

Fortunately a record survives[24] of No 5020s running with the very heavy train on 7 September (Table 5). With the extremely limited familiarisation on the part of the crew, it was a very creditable piece of work to breast the 1 in 335 to Tring at 54½ (about 1,180EDBHP). This effort had certainly not winded No 5020, for she ran fast down to Bletchley. The engine was then eased somewhat to avoid gaining time, but to pass Roade at 52 and clear the hump at Kilsby Tunnel at nothing lower than 55 was very good work. From Stafford No 5020 gave another indication of her potential when pushed, with no lower speed on the 1 in 398 to Whitmore than 61½, needing something like 1,290EDBHP — impressive for a low-superheat 4-6-0 with 27.8sq ft of grate.

During the following week, No 5020 ran freight trials on the 20.28 FF2 Manchester-Camden and 19.00 FF1[25] Camden-Manchester, the booked loads for which were 55 and 50 vans, probably about 610 and 560 tons, respectively. On 12 September the 20.28 train was specially loaded to 60 vans, about 660 tons. Coal used was again Grimethorpe Grade 1.

The interim report makes no comment on timekeeping, but records that 15-20% cutoff with full regulator was the normal working method, with 30-45% on the principal rising grades. The steaming of the boiler was uniform and satisfactory throughout'. It concluded:

'... the two-cylinder 4-6-0 engine appears to be a very efficient and satisfactory mixed traffic power unit',

Table 5
14.40 Euston-Liverpool. 7 September 1934 Dynamometer Car Test
Locomotive: Class 5 4-6-0 No 5020
Load: 15 coaches, 468 tons tare, 495 tons gross
Driver: Not recorded

Distance miles		Schedule minutes	Actual Time min sec	Speeds
0.0	Euston	0	0.00	Not banked
1.0	mp 1		3.23	
5.4	Willesden Jc	9	9.52	—
8.1	Wembley		12.29	58½
13.2	Hatch End		18.15	—
17.5	Watford Jc	22	22.35	—
21.0	Kings Langley		25.27	—
28.0	Berkhamsted		33.09	—
31.7	Tring	38	37.14	54½ min
40.2	Leighton Buzzard		44.27	77 max
46.7	Bletchley	51	49.42	—
59.9	Roade	63	61.43	52 min
62.8	Blisworth	66	64.44	—
	Kilsby Tunnel		—	55 min
			signals	
82.6	Rugby	88	85.56	
14.5	Nuneaton	16	16.03	75
27.4	Tamworth	29	27.37	—
33.7	Lichfield	35	33.41	55 min
41.7	Rugeley	43	41.32	—
51.0	Stafford	53	50.41	*
56.3	Norton Bridge	60	56.32	—
60.8	Standon Bridge		—	63
65.0	Whitmore	69	64.54	61½ min
70.7	Betley Road		69.59	78
			signal stop	
75.5	Crewe	80	78.19	

Net Times: Euston-Rugby 85min
Rugby-Crewe 76min
*Permanent Speed Restriction

words which were to be echoed by countless thousands of enginemen over the next three decades and more.

The recorded coal consumptions ranged between 3.28 and 3.48lb/DBHP hr on the passenger workings, and between 2.68 and 2.85lb/DBHP hr on the freight, while the water consumptions were between 23.6 and 28.2lb/DBHP hr. These figures were so low, in relation to an engine producing steam at little over 500°F, as to invite disbelief. As will be seen now, when the first tests with 'Jubilees' were made immediately after this, a similar situation arose (one wonders whether the gross inaccuracy found on the No 1 dynamometer car in 1928[26] was being repeated). These tests, between Wolverhampton and Euston, involved also the nearly-new parallel-boilered 'Patriots', which had already overtaken most of the train working on this line. The objective was stated as:

'To obtain information as to the capabilities of the three-cylinder 4-6-0 type engines . . . working . . . at special accelerated timings produced by the Chief Operating Manager.'

These tests extended from 17 September to 6 December, using 'Jubilees' Nos 5553, 5554 and 5556 along with 'Patriots' Nos 5517, 5540 and 5551.

As compared with the normal 2 hour schedule to and from Birmingham, with one (Up) and two (Down) stops, four alternative Up schedules were worked, in 110min (one stop) and 115min (two stops), and two Down schedules in 117min (two stops), with loadings aimed at 310-320 tons. A preliminary report No 50B of October 1934, for CME internal use, drew attention to the very hard work involved in these accelerated

timings, notably in the Down direction, where the cutoffs needed were:

Euston-Camden	55%
Camden-Willesden	35%
Watford-Tring	25%
Blisworth-Rugby	35%

Commenting on one particular run, the report said:

'. . . the engine was worked almost to its maximum capacity from Euston to Cheddington . . . From Bletchley to Roade the horsepower rose to a maximum of 915 just before shutting off to stop at Blisworth. Leaving Blisworth 1,000HP was developed while accelerating and 860HP was maintained until approaching Rugby . . .'

And surprisingly described the steaming as 'good, in spite of the high demand on the boiler . . .' The smokebox contained excessive ash each day, a sure sign of potential trouble; on some days it built up to above the centre of the smokebox door. Official reaction to the consumption figures of 3.51lb/DBHP hr for No 5556 and 3.58lb/DBHP hr for No 5551 was evidently sceptical, for the tests continued.

The difference in steaming between No 5020 and the 'Jubilees' spoke for itself, and immediately concentrated attention on the 'Jubilee' draughting. During December a CME representative was riding on No 5556 on the same test trains, making successive minor alterations in the smokebox to effect an improvement — a 5in jumper cap, later lowered to 6in below centreline, with a modified chimney and petticoat to suit. Finally the jumper cap was weighted down to reduce the lift at any given pressure, but none of these changes brought the steaming up to satisfactory standards.

Dynamometer Car Report No 50 of 24 January 1935 dealt with the further testing between 29 October and 6 December, (totally ignoring the work done in September and most of October) with 'Patriots' Nos 5517 and 5540 and 'Jubilees' Nos 5553, 5554 and 5578, normally with about 320 tons but on three days with 373 and 380 tons. It presented a very different picture from that in the interim report. The steaming of the 'Patriots' was 'very good throughout'. On No 5552 (standard 5⅛in jumper blastpipe) and No 5554 (5in jumper cap weighted down) 'some difficulty was experienced in maintaining full boiler pressure although timekeeping was usually satisfactory'. On the Down trains, from Euston to Tring:

'. . . a sustained power output of 850DBHP is maintained for long periods, which is considered to be approaching the maximum power available . . . there is little reserve of power . . .'

Coal and water consumptions can be summarised as follows:

	'Patriot'		'Jubilee'	
	Max	Min	Max	Min
Train load, tons Up	373	305	373	311
Down	346	302	380	312
Coal:lb/mile	42.3	37.6	49.7	39.2
lb/DBHP hr	3.73	3.48	4.44	3.92
Water:gal/mile	33.0	30.0	36.0	31.5
lb/DBHP hr	28.1	26.7	31.7	29.8
Evaporation:lb/lb coal	8.3	7.22	8.05*	7.09*

*Figures for two days omitted due to injector defects, etc.

The 'Jubilee' consumptions on a DBHP hr basis were significantly worse than those of the 'Patriots' under similar conditions, which is entirely what could be expected, given the superheat levels.

The general conclusion reached was that:

'... the timing schedules given ... (with the modifications suggested ...) can be worked successfully under normal running conditions, with 5X engines in good mechanical condition with train loads of approximately 300 tons.'

While true for the 'Patriots', the unresolved steaming problems of the 'Jubilees' made this conclusion seem either optimistic or over diplomatic!

Meanwhile, during October a fresh series of dynamometer car trials with a Class 5 on fitted freight work had been conducted, the selected engine being No 5036 (with line 1 boiler). These used the 14.55 Camden-Carlisle, worked as FF1 to Crewe and FF2 forward, and loaded to 50 vans, about 560 tons, returning on the 15.30 FF1 Carlisle-Broad Street as far as Willesden, and loading to 34 vans, about 403 tons. Grade 1 coal was used, and in the Down direction rear end assistance was provided from Oxenholme to Grayrigg and from Tebay to Shap Summit. Timekeeping left something to be desired, and there was criticism in the interim report that the enginemanship did not always rise to requirements. For instance, from Carnforth to Oxenholme (12.9 miles, 22min pass-to-stop, 35.2mph average) it was recognised that 'the maximum sustained power development of the engine would be required' (calculated at no less than 912 DBHP average!), yet on 15 October the actual running time was 31.05min with an actual average DBHP of only 516. There was clearly little effective control over the footplate work. In the opposite direction the worst — and hardly surprising — shortfalls were in the start from Upperby to Plumpton (11.8 miles, 18min start-to-pass, 39.5mph average, which would have required 984DBHP and was utterly impossible on the gradients), and from Crewe up to Whitmore (10.5 miles, 15min start-to-pass, 42mph average, which was the postwar passenger 'XL Limit' timing!).

Steaming of the engine was at all times good. Consumptions were:

	14.55 Camden-Carlisle		15.30 Carlisle-Broad Street	
	10 Oct	15 Oct	11 Oct	16 Oct
Coal:lb/mile	64.8	65.2	41.7	46.7
lb/DBHP hr	4.13	4.16	3.27	3.73
lb/sq ft/hr	71.2	67.7	53.6	60.1
Water:gall/mile	41.6	43.6	34.7	37.1*
lb/DBHP hr	26.5	27.9	26.9	28.8
Evaporation:lb/lb coal	6.42	6.69	8.31	7.93

*Excessive due to exhaust steam injector not picking up cleanly.

These specific consumptions, 40% (coal) and 11% (water) greater than those of the earlier freight tests, seem much more in line with expectations for this type of engine and work.

Here, then, were test results on new Stanier engines showing specific coal consumption broadly in the 4.0-4.5lb/DBHP hr range, figures more reminiscent of pre-grouping designs and well bettered by their LMS predecessors. Clearly the original thinking on superheaters had to be revised for both classes, while continuing to seek an optimum draughting layout for the 'Jubilees'. So a group of five of these engines

from current production, Nos 5642-5646, was outshopped from Crewe in December 1934 with modified tubeplates, etc, providing a 21-element superheater (Table 3, line 2), and a similar modification on Class 5s was introduced from the start of Vulcan's second order (February 1935) and from No 5007 at Crewe in March; Armstrong Whitworth brought it in on all their 100-engine order from May. The use of 2in dia small tubes was continued, giving reasonably good A/S and total free gas area/grate area ratios.

No 5642, the first of this batch and barely run in, was used for a quick one-day dynamometer car trial between Wolverhampton and Euston on accelerated timings with 366 and 356 tons. Steaming was 'not quite adequate', a minimum pressure of 195lb/sq in being recorded on the Down journey at Cheddington, but the specific coal and water consumptions were down to 3.68 and 26.6lb/DBHP hr respectively, comparable with 'Patriot' figures.

Tests in 1935

There was a short pause to digest the results so far, before testing was resumed in February 1935, with further dynamometer car trials with 'Jubilees' between Wolverhampton and Euston; the accelerated timings used in December 1934 were again used, but on one day standard timings, with loadings up to 420 tons, applied. The engines involved were:

No 5646 with line 2 boiler and 4¾in weighted jumper blastpipe cap 3in below centreline with modified chimney. The grate was altered to give a more uniform slope, and the smokebox deflector plates were also modified.

No 5556 with the curious line 3 boiler in which the small tubes *below the superheater* were increased to 2⅛in dia. 5in (27 February) and 5⅛in (28 February) weighted jumper blastpipe caps were used, lowered to 7in below centreline; the same modified chimney, grate and deflector plates were fitted.

The engines were generally worked at about 22% cutoff with full regulator, except in the case of the 420-ton train, when 28% was needed. Timekeeping was not quite adequate.

The Report indicated that:

'... steaming was good with all the engines, but engine No 5556 was slightly freer in steaming than engine No 5646, particularly when the former engine had a 5in blastpipe. With a 5⅛in blastpipe engine No 5556 steamed well and no difficulty should be experienced in working the accelerated services with trains loads of about 300 tons, although there is more reserve in steaming capacity with a 5in blastpipe cap.'

No 5646, with 21 elements, showed a specific coal consumption of 3.89lb/DBHP hr on accelerated timings, a saving of 7% over No 5556 (14 elements). As compared with the earlier engines, both the poor efficiency and the steaming problems were beginning to yield to solution.

From this base, yet another test series on the Wolverhampton-Euston line was organised, in April, this time using no less than five locomotives, to compare performance and coal and water consumptions with the 'Patriots'. The engines were No 5645 and 5646, with 21 elements but with tubes modified as line 4, 5in dia weighted jumper cap and modified smokebox deflector plates, No 5556 in the same condition as in February, and 'Patriots' Nos 5518 and 5525. The tests were run on normal two hour timings to and from Birmingham and made up to 350 tons where practicable.

Dynamometer Car Report No 53 of April/May 1935 shows that sectional timekeeping was excellent in the Up direction, though not quite so good on the harder Down trains. The 'Jubilees' used marginally longer cutoffs than the two 'Patriots', 27% being typical of the climbs to Tring and Roade. The steaming was 'very good' on all five engines. With Nos 5645 and 5646:

'... the usual method of firing was to maintain a fairly heavy fire, ... somewhat thicker at the firehole door, and to use the back damper, but on the Down trips from Euston to Tring it was found that slightly freer steaming was obtained by the use of the front damper.'

Using the back damper only, the ashpan 'hump' over the trailing axle partly shielded the front of the grate from the primary air flow, reducing the combustion rate there and thus the maximum output, as will be seen later, but this suited many firemen, who then needed to feed little coal to the front of the grate.

The average coal and water consumptions were:

	5645, 5646 21 elements	5556 14 elements	5518, 5525 Standard
Coal: lb/mile	37.0	43.4	38.4
lb/DBHP hr	3.34	3.71	3.41
Water: gal/mile	28.0	35.4	30.8
lb/DBHP hr	25.3	30.2	27.4
Evaporation: lb/lb coal	7.56	8.14	8.02

The larger superheater on No 5645 and 5646 had reduced the specific coal and water consumptions as compared with the low-superheat No 5556 by averages of 8.9% (coal) and 16.2% (water).

The Report drew perhaps unduly precise conclusions from rather loosely controlled dynamometer car tests, but broadly the straight throatplate '3A' boiler with 21 elements and fairly effective draughting had reached the standards which the 'Patriots' had set some five years previously.

While this testing of 'Jubilees' had been going on, the Class 5s had not been neglected. But it was surprising that, for comparative purposes against a parallel-boilered 2-6-0 on fitted freight work over the Settle & Carlisle line in March, it was No 5048, a 14-element engine with line 1 boiler, which was selected rather than one of the new 21-element engines from Vulcan Foundry. The 2-6-0 chosen, No 2831, failed with a hot coupled axlebox after her second run to Carlisle and was replaced by No 2751 for the final day. The trains worked were the 19.30 FF1 Sheffield (Wicker)-Carlisle, allowed 45 vans plus dynamometer car and brake, returning with the 16.00 FF2 Carlisle-Masboro', allowed 50 vans, etc, on the following day. In practice, the loadings of the Down train varied from 492 to 560 tons, and in the Up direction from 547 to 596 tons as far as Skipton. Grimethorpe Grade 1 coal was used.

Dynamometer Car Report No 54 notes that on the main 1 in 100 climbs to Blea Moor and Ais Gill the Class 5 was working at cutoffs of 40, 45 and 50%, while the 2-6-0 managed with 35 and 40% and only brief periods of 45%.

DBHPs southbound from Carlisle were generally around 900 and 800 to Appleby for 4-6-0 and 2-6-0 respectively, and on the 1 in 100 to Ais Gill they were generaly in the ranges 800-900 and 700-800. Minimum speeds at the summit were 14mph with the 2-6-0 hauling 593 tons and 16mph with No 5048 on 596 tons (Fig 6).

'The steaming of all the engines . . ., on normal gradients, was quite satisfactory, while on the severe gradients the pressures were on the whole well maintained.'
but that
'. . . the loadings appear to be fully up to what is practicable for these engines on the grades'.

The overall consumption figures show that the 2-6-0 was decidedly more economical than the Class 5, and the Report was quite blunt on the subject:

'The decrease in consumption in the case of the . . . 2-6-0 engine is attributable mainly to a higher degree of superheat and to a somewhat more economical steam distribution in the cylinders . . .'

The latter remark presumably based on the ability of the 2-6-0 to work on shorter cutoffs due to its higher tractive effort.

	5048	2831/2751	Diff for 2-6-0
Coal: lb/mile	66.7	55.0	−17.5%
lb/DHBP hr	3.89	3.43	−11.8%
lb/sq ft grate/hr	77.7	66.3	
Water: gal/mile	51.2	45.4	−11.3%
lb/DBHP hr	29.9	28.3	− 5.3%
Evaporation: lb/lb coal	7.7	8.25	+ 7.1%

So here was Stanier's new workhorse beaten into second place by the Hughes design dating from 10 years earlier.

A further series of tests was set up for the following month, remitted to make a direct comparison of the general performance, coal and water consumptions of 14- and 21-element engines. The machines selected were:

No 5067 with line 1 boiler and standard 5⅛in jumper blastpipe, and
No 5079 with the curious line 4 boiler having 2⅛in tubes, with 5¼in jumper blastpipe.

Besides working the same freight trains between Sheffield and Carlisle as previously, the two engines each worked the 10.00 St Pancras-Leeds and 18.00 Leeds-St Pancras express passenger trains, 'Special Limit' trains for which a Class 5's loading was 300 tons. Actual loads were:

	5067	5079
19.30 FF1 Sheffield-Carlisle*	514 tons	562 tons
16.00 FF2 Carlisle-Masborough†	606 tons	610 tons
10.00 St Pancras-Leeds	275 tons	279 tons
08.00 Leeds-St Pancras‡	311 tons	312 tons

* From Masborough † To Skipton ‡ From Sheffield

Dynamometer Car Report No 55 records that on the 16.00 from Carlisle, No 5067 ran the 29 gruelling miles from the Durran Hill start to the water stop at Appleby in 58¾min

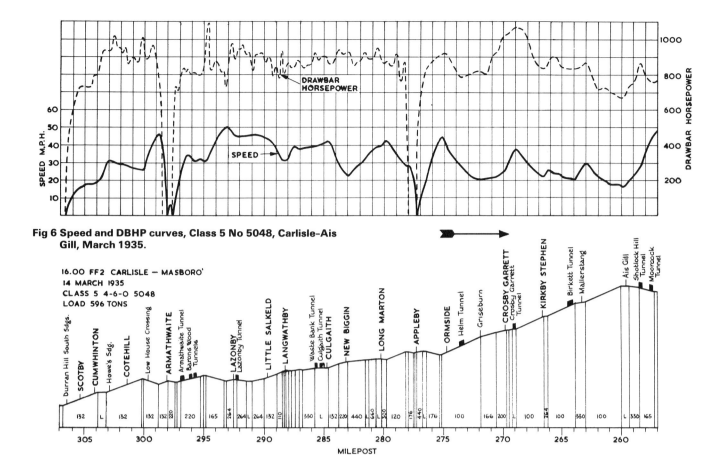

Fig 6 Speed and DBHP curves, Class 5 No 5048, Carlisle–Ais Gill, March 1935.

16.00 FF2 CARLISLE – MASBORO'
14 MARCH 1935
CLASS 5 4-6-0 5048
LOAD 596 TONS

(63min allowed), while No 5079 took 64¾min including a signal stop at New Biggin. Cutoffs averaged 35-45% and 30-35% respectively on this section. Onward to Ais Gill summit No 5079 practically kept the 45min timing for the 17.6 miles, hammering away on cutoffs of 45-60%.

On the passenger workings, the 'Special Limit' timings were kept without difficulty, much of the work being done on 20-25% cutoff. 5079 ran up from Leicester, 99.1 miles, in 103min net, while in the Down direction with No 5067 Leicester was reached in about 102min net. Steaming was good throughout with both engines, with the 'usual method of firing, ie a moderate fire on the grate which was thickened under the firehole door'. The back damper only was used.

Coal and water consumption figures were:

	Fitted freight		Exp Pass		Overall		
	5067	5079	5067	5079	5067	5079	% gain by 5079
Coal: lb/mile	62.4	55.7	39.7	34.7	49.5	43.7	−11.7%
lb/DBHP hr	3.78	3.13	4.22	3.38	3.97	3.23	−18.6%
Water: gal/mile	48.4	41.5	30.3	26.3	38.2	32.8	−14.1%
lb/DBHP hr	29.3	23.3	32.3	25.6	30.6	24.3	−20.6%
Evaporation:lb/lb coal	7.76	7.44	7.67	7.54	7.72	7.49	− 3.0%

It will be seen that the fitted freight figures for No 5067 closely corresponded with those for No 5048 a month earlier, thus confirming the future course towards high superheat.

With the 'Jubilees', however, the final solution was less clearly apparent. In fact, so concerned were the Motive Power authorities under D. C. Urie that in September 1935, immediately prior to the introduction of the 115min Euston-Birmingham service all the 'Patriots' on the Midland Div-

ision, except for three at Leeds used over the Carlisle line, were transferred to the Western Division (Camden, Aston and Bushbury) to work these trains, in exchange for 'Jubilees';[27] at this stage of development the latter were regarded as insufficiently reliable to entrust with such a prestige service, and they did not return to these trains until 1939.

While all this specific testing of the two classes had been in progress, separate and largely unpublicised tests were being conducted between Crewe and Carlisle, at the instigation of the Advisory Committee on Scientific Research, to provide information on the efficiency of several different configurations of 'Jubilee' boiler in comparison with those of 'Royal Scots' and 'Patriots'. The engines used were:

No 5558 in March on freight work with line 1 boiler. Following this trial the boiler was evidently changed quickly for one built for the last 'Jubilee' then under construction, with tubeplates to line 3. This boiler was tested on passenger trains from 20 March to 1 May.

No 5645 in May and June on passenger trains, now carrying a line 5 boiler.

Steam temperatures under stable conditions were low; No 5558 with line 1 boiler did not better 507°F, while the line 3 boiler temperatures were even lower, with nothing over 486°F, whereas No 5645 with line 5 boiler could only produce a maximum of 554°F. However, the 'Patriot' was little better at up to 565°F.

With both 'Jubilees', pressures on five out of eight recorded occasions on the climb to Shap Summit were below

29

200lb/sq in, down to as low as 182lb/sq in. By contrast the 'Patriot' (nominal pressure 200lb/sq in) was doing almost all its work on these sections at 195lb/sq in or more. While the heat balance for the four boilers did not differ greatly, the report was able to comment that:

No 5558 Line 1 and Line 3 boilers.
'The difference between the two boilers ... is in favour of the 2in tubes ... In the case of the (line 3) boiler, more gas passes through the enlarged small tubes and therefore less through the large tubes ...' Likewise the heat absorption by the small tubes decreased, resulting in greater losses to the chimney.
No 5645 Line 5 boiler.
'An increase in the number of superheater elements causes a decrease in the heat absorbed ... through the small tubes.' However, the total heat absorbed was marginally better than with either the line 1 or line 3 configurations.

The Report on these tests is dated 8 October 1935, and clearly its salient features would have been known earlier. It is therefore remarkable (knowing the speed with which Crewe Works *could* react to required changes in tubeplate layouts) that all new 'Jubilees' built from November 1935 to April 1936, save one — a total of 35 engines — should have been turned out with $2\frac{1}{8}$in tubes which, shorter in the sloping throatplate boiler, gave a totally unsuitable A/S ratio of 1/338.

The next tests for attention took place between 17 June and 11 July 1935, firstly between Crewe and Euston, and then between Crewe and Carlisle, for the purpose of:

'... determining the maximum loading for various classes of engines working express passenger "Limited Load" trains.'

The trains used were the 11.08 Crewe-Euston (with six intermediate stops) and 17.20 Euston-Crewe (with two stops), and on the northern section the 09.31 Crewe-Carlisle (a semi-fast with eight intermediate stops) and 15.57 Carlisle-Crewe (with three stops). The engines chosen were 'Jubilee' 5646, with line 2 boiler, and Class 5 No 5082 with line 2 boiler. The engines worked two days on each train with 30 tons over and two days with 45 tons over the permitted 'Limited Load' tonnages of:

	Jubilee	*Class 5*
Euston-Carnforth	430	380
Carnforth-Carlisle	365	320

Dynamometer Car Report No 58 of July 1935 relates that on the Crewe-Euston tests the steaming of both engines was either 'very' or 'completely' satisfactory. The 'Jubilee' was worked very hard up to Whitmore, but elsewhere 20-25% cutoff was more usual. The Class 5 was taken more easily to Whitmore, at 25-30% cutoff, but otherwise was driven similarly, with full regulator. Between Crewe and Carlisle, however, the position was somewhat different; the steaming of the Class 5 was still 'completely satisfactory throughout', whereas with the 'Jubilee':

'The steaming on the easier gradients and on the level was satisfactory. On the harder gradients full pressure was not

maintained, which was *attributable to the high demand made on the boiler*', and 'Difficulty was experienced in maintaining a working level of water in the boiler under these conditions'.

The italics are mine! Pressures down to 190lb/sq in were recorded, and clearly the fireman was worried how far he dare mortgage the boiler. From Tebay up to Summit a maximum cutoff of 55% was used, while on the north approach to the Summit 30-40% was common. Attention was drawn to somewhat erratic timekeeping by both engines, though this was mainly an indictment of the timetable for asking the impossible. No 5646 was regularly sustaining 920-970 average DBHP south of Crewe, and the Class 5 was also sustaining DBHPs of up to 910. On the 09.31 Crewe-Carlisle:

'... load 414 tons, engine 5646 ... lost $1\frac{1}{4}$min from Oxenholme to Tebay, the sustained average DBHP between Oxenholme and Grayrigg being 844, whilst over the same section, taking ... 374 tons, the mixed traffic engine kept running time, the average DBHP between Oxenholme and Grayrigg being 834.'

Coal and water consumptions averaged as follows:

	Crewe-Euston		Crewe-Carlisle	
	5646	*5082*	*5646*	*5082*
Coal: lb/DBHP hr	3.28	3.01	3.04	2.95
lb/sq ft/hr	81.5	71.8	66.8	67.7
Water: lb/DBHP hr	23.3	22.9	24.2*	22.1
Evaporation: lb/lb coal	7.12	7.63	7.94	7.84

* High due to exhaust steam injector wasting water.

Thus the Class 5 consistently bettered the 'Jubilee' in efficiency, and was not far behind in maximum output.

The conclusion drawn was a wholly realistic one:

'... it is not considered it would be economically sound, either from the operation or the maintenance point of view, for the loadings of these engines to be increased beyond the present standard "Limited Loads" on the Euston-Crewe-Carlisle route.'

This stood the test of time, for these loadings were never altered with steam traction; particularly under hard steaming conditions on Grayrigg and Shap banks the 'Jubilees' were not yet fully up to handling the existing loads.

But the evidence in favour of high superheat was overwhelming, and the decision was taken during 1935 that new engines of both classes would get redesigned boilers which, in addition to larger superheaters, would have larger grate area — a byproduct of reducing the foundation ring width from $3\frac{3}{4}$in to 3in — a sloping throatplate with smaller tubes, and separate dome and topfeed. These features were built into 'Jubilees' from No 5665 and Class 5s from No 5225, together with all spare boilers. Eleven 'Jubilees' and 13 Class 5s built with straight throatplate boilers received modifications to frame stretchers in front of the firebox to enable sloping throatplate boilers to be fitted, providing a 'float' of straight throatplate boilers for exchange at General Repairs. The first 'Jubilee' with the new line 11 boiler, No 5665, emerged from Crewe in November 1935, but with its $1\frac{7}{8}$in tubes it was a loner, for the next 37 engines had the retrograde 2⅛in tubes, though with other variations (lines 12, 13 and 14).

Tests in 1936

Testing restarted in earnest in February 1936, but some preliminary work done on No 5665, and described in an internal report of 30 January, is of interest. In the ashpan, with the front damper shut and back damper open, the pressure in the rear portion was approximately atmospheric, while in the part forward of the axle 'hump' there was a vacuum of 0.75in wg. With an average firebox vacuum of 1.5in wg this meant that the pressure difference through the firebed (ie the combustion stimulus) on the front half of the grate was only half of that on the back section.

Dynamometer car testing resumed on 20 February on the Wolverhampton-Euston route to assess the effect of the latest boiler modifications, and lasted until 13 March. Loadings south of Birmingham ranged between 331 and 383 tons. The engines used were:

No 5669 with line 12 boiler. On three days she had a 4½in blastpipe cap 11½in below centreline, and modifications were made to the grate and brick arch. On two days a 4¾in blastpipe cap at the same height was fitted, and grate and brick arch returned to standard.

No 5684 with line 12 boiler on 3, 4 and 5 March. The 4½in blastpipe cap was 8½in below centreline, and the grate and brick arch modified as on No 5669.

No 5665 with line 11 boiler on 12 and 13 March. A 4¾in blastpipe cap was 11½in below centreline, and the grate and brick arch modified as on No 5669. In addition, new firedoors admitting more secondary air were fitted.

Dynamometer Car Report No 62 notes that the steaming of No 5665 was completely satisfactory, with no pressure below 221lb/sq in, as was that of No 5669 with either blastpipe cap. No 5684 suffered a leaking smokebox joint throughout and her steaming was thus somewhat shy in the Down direction when having to work hard; in retrospect one wonders why the fault was not corrected when detected. The recorded coal and water consumptions were:

stepped up to 24 elements and with 1⅞in tubes, introduced from No 5702 in May 1936 and standardised for tubeplate renewals on both straight and sloping throatplate boilers (lines 9 and 15). At last it appeared that the way was clear to the 'Jubilees' becoming very capable medium-sized 4-6-0s, even if their efficiency fell a little short of that of the Class 5s.

Tests in 1937

It would seem that doubts still lingered, derived from earlier tests, that what might be all right south of Preston was not necessarily good enough in the fell country. A short series of tests was therefore arranged in March 1937 between Crewe and Carlisle, using No 5740, fitted with line 15 boiler from new and with the newly proved draughting. The trains hauled were the 13.09 Crewe-Carlisle, loading to 318/323 tons, and the 08.30 Carlisle-Crewe semi-fast, loading to 265 tons ex-Carlisle, 362 tons ex-Oxenholme and 455 tons from Preston (these were the days of through portions!). Dynamometer Car Report No 69 indicates that timekeeping presented no difficulties, and the steaming:

'was excellent, full boiler pressure being maintained without difficulty under the severest conditions. The general cutoff employed on the level and easier gradients was 16-25%, and on the heavier gradients 35-50%.

Steam temperatures averaged 600°F, with a maximum of 640°F. Smokebox vacuum reached a maximum of 6.4in wg at 35% cutoff at 44mph.

Coal and water consumptions were:

	16/17 March	18/19 March
Coal: lb/mile	43.0	42.6
lb/DBHP hr	3.51	3.66
lb/sq ft/hr	63.8	63.6
Water: gal/mile	33.7	33.9
lb/DBHP hr	27.4	29.1
Evaporation: lb/lb coal	7.84	7.98

which the report described as 'satisfactory'; it also commented that:

'From an analysis of the indicator diagram (sic) the distribution of the steam was quite satisfactory, and the running resistance of the engine was normal.'

Engine	5669					5684			5665	
Boiler line No	12					12			11	
Blastpipe dia	4½in			4¾in		4½in			4¾in	
Date	20/2	21/2	6/3	10/3	11/3	3/3	4/3	5/3	12/3	13/3
Coal: lb/DBHP hr	3.78	3.69	4.14	3.87	4.09	3.98	3.91	3.90	3.62	3.66
Water: lb/DBHP hr	27.5	27.1	27.7	27.6	27.9	27.3	27.0	26.5	24.9	25.1
Evaporation: lb/lb coal	7.26	7.34	6.70	7.16	6.81	6.83	6.91	6.81	6.89	6.87
Steam Temps °F										
Average	580-595			550-570		550-580			585-600	
Maximum	605			585		585			605	

From these results there was little hesitation in deciding that the line 11 boiler, with 4¾in blastpipe cap 11½in below centreline, and deeper firedoors to admit more secondary air, was superior to the other variants tested in steaming, superheat and specific coal and water consumptions. The Report, having said this, dismissed the grate and brick arch alterations as not advantageous, and concluded that 'subsequent further improvements to the tube and superheater arrangement have been introduced and made standard . . .'. This referred to the line 15 arrangement, with superheater

Oh, that bland word 'satisfactory' — how often it appeared in these reports!

The following month, No 5740 plus dynamometer car went to Bushbury to run further tests on the much-travelled Wolverhampton-Euston route, with loadings of 351/362 tons Up and 332/336 tons Down to Birmingham, on 12-15 April 1937. Report No 69 recorded that:

'Throughout the tests the steaming of the engine was most satisfactory. On the first trip from Wolverhampton . . . the front damper was used, but for the remainder of the test the back damper only, and a medium thick fire was used. The general cutoff employed was 22-25%, with full regulator . . .'

Timekeeping was 'very satisfactory', and demonstrated 'the ability of the engine to make up running time . . . without being worked heavily'.

The coal and water consumptions were compared with 'Patriot' performances on the same trains in April 1935, by implication dismissing all previous 'Jubilee' tests on this route as unrepresentative of the engines' potential. They were:

	Max	Min	Average	'Patriots' April 1935
Coal: lb/mile	39.4	37.0	38.1	40.1
lb/DBHP hr	3.20	3.11	3.16	3.51
Water: gal/mile	30.4	27.6	28.8	31.7
lb/DBHP hr	24.2	23.5	23.9	27.7
Evaporation: lb/lb coal	7.71	7.43	7.58	7.89

Now, at last, it could be claimed that the 'Jubilee' had proved itself as a competent and economical locomotive, particularly so in fast running on an easily graded route. Henceforward, further testing with the 'Jubilees' was almost exclusively devoted to showing their prowess in handling the mile-a-minute accelerated timings on the Midland Division; this will be dealt with in the next chapter. Nevertheless, two further test series are worth mentioning for the sake of completeness.

In May/June 1937, No 5633, with original line 1 boiler, was tested on the Derby-St Pancras and Derby-Bristol routes to assess the effect of increasing valve lead to $5/16$in and streamlining the valve heads. In addition, two larger blastpipe caps fitted with cruciform bars were compared with the now standard $4\frac{3}{4}$in plain cap; these were $5\frac{5}{16}$in and $5\frac{1}{16}$in dia, equivalent in area to plain caps of 5in and $4\frac{3}{4}$in dia.

It is noteworthy that this trial started only two months after the steam distribution on No 5740 had been pronounced 'quite satisfactory', though an internal memorandum on the new tests mentions (presumably referring to No 5740) that '. . . the original cards showed rather a tendency to leanness . . .' An extract from the summary of indicator card results is given below:

Cutoff %	Speed mph	Ratio $\dfrac{MEP}{Boiler\ Pressure}$ %		
		Standard $\frac{1}{4}$in lead	Streamlined $\frac{1}{4}$in lead	Standard $\frac{5}{16}$in lead
15	60	20.1	20.5	22.5
20	45	31.0	33.4	33.9
20	60	26.8*	24.5	25.5
25	40	32.9	34.2	36.5
25	55	28.6	29.3	32.1
30	40	33.6	40.1	40.6
Average of tests		28.7	31.1	32.6

* This figure appears to be a misprint for 23.8.

The improvement in mean effective pressure with increased lead led to its immediate adoption for the 'Royal Scot'/'Jubilee'/'Patriot' family, though not elsewhere. The cruciform blastpipe caps had little effect on smokebox vacuum but tended to increase the back pressure, and led to excessive quantities of ash in the smokebox.

But there were still influences at work seeking better draughting, and in June 1937 No 5684 emerged from Crewe works after her first Service Repair fitted with a double

'Kylchap' KC blastpipe for the line 12 boiler.[28] In the first half of November she underwent dynamometer car trials between Wolverhampton and Euston. These covered three sizes of blastpipe 'wedges', though Dynamometer Car Report No 73 fails to give any dimensions. In view of the results, there must remain serious doubt whether the blastpipe and chimney were correctly proportioned to the boiler. After recording that the intermediate size wedges gave the best result in steaming, the Report continues:

' . . . it was found advisable to run with a thick fire, as there was a distinct tendency, when working heavily, to tear holes in the fire. This was a marked feature when using the large size of wedges. Except when working lightly there was a continuous stream of incandescent fuel ejected from the chimney, and at the end of each test (254 miles) the smokebox was filled with ash almost to the level of the blastpipe tops, but the total amount was not excessive. The fact that there is more spark throwing than with a normal engine can only be attributed to the larger area of the chimney, the petticoat arrangement and the larger surface area of the inducing jet . . .'

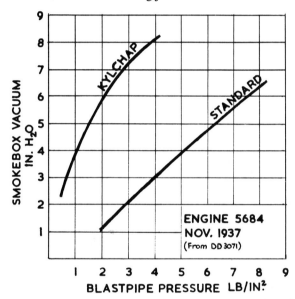

Fig 7 Graph of smokebox vacuum/blastpipe pressure. No 5684 (Kylchap) and standard engines.

a comment which might be challenged. Certainly the graph of smokebox vacuum against blastpipe pressure (Fig 7) shows such a vast increase with the Kylchap blastpipe as to probably be excessive. The high average firing rate of 93lb/sq ft/hr on the Down working was hardly enough to justify the pyrotechnics at the chimney. The coal and water consumptions differed little from those recorded with the same engine in February/March 1936 with $4\frac{1}{2}$in single blastpipe, though there was some evidence of a marginal increase in superheat. The arrangement was not persevered with, and came off next year.

So ends the prewar saga of the 4-6-0 boilers. In the case of the Class 5s, it could truly be said that, in steaming and economy, they lived happily ever after. The 'Jubilees' were pronounced equally successful, if never quite so economical, and were promptly pushed in at the deep end to be the mainstay of accelerated passenger services on the Midland Division and elsewhere. Only in the postwar period did this shining image show unmistakable signs of tarnish.

Above: No 5574, unnamed and also with taller chimney, accelerates her Down express past Kilburn No 1 box.
E. R. Wethersett

Left: Resplendent in her new black and chrome special livery, 'Jubilee' No 5552 *Silver Jubilee* — built as No 5642 — heads north through Kilburn High Road in May 1935 on a running-in trip. It will be seen that the topfeed cover on this engine was unique in being a larger-than-standard dome without separate clackbox covers.
E. R. Wethersett/Real Photos 24400

Below left: No 5677 *Beatty* is in charge of a 10-coach Down express on Bushey troughs. In this 1937 scene the fireman has clearly fired round the box and closed the firehole doors while he busies himself with taking water.
Real Photos 24119

33

Above: Working a Down excursion to Leicester in 1935, 'Jubilee' No 5652 appears to be giving Bushey troughs a miss. All the 10 coaches visible appear to be either ex-LNWR or ex-Midland vehicles.
Real Photos 24117

Right On the Up 'Lakes Express' from Keswick and Windermere, on Bushey troughs in 1936, a pair of 'Jubilees', Nos 5553 and 5605, both unnamed, are under easy steam as the train engine takes water.
E. R. Wethersett

Below right: 'Jubilee' No 5647, devoid of nameplates, has a lengthy express freight train passing Rugeley in 1935, but the fireman is able to take a breather. *W. L. Good*

Top: On the Midland Division in July 1935, the 16.25
St Pancras-Manchester express is in charge of unnamed
'Jubilee' No 5635 just north of Mill Hill.
E. R. Wethersett/Real Photos 24388

Above: No 5642 *Boscawen* is briefly on 1 in 67 as she roars past
Kingswood Junction with the 10-coach Up 'Devonian' in the
summer of 1936. There is a white feather at the safety valves
— but for how long? Built as No 5552, she still carries a
14-element boiler at this time. *Real Photos 3865*

Below: No 5684 *Jutland* in 1937, fitted with double Kylchap blastpipe and chimney. With such an illustrious name, is it surprising that she emitted 'a continuous stream of incandescent fuel . . . from the chimney? *BR LM Region*

Bottom: With only three miles to go, No 5163 drifts past Kilburn No 1 box in charge of an Up Birmingham express in 1936. *Real Photos 24079*

Above: No 5042 makes a smoky exit from Elstree Tunnel on a Down Manchester express in 1935. *Real Photos 24077*

Left: No 5043 has a light six-coach train — including a venerable non-corridor coach behind the tender — on a Down express between Northfield and Halesowen Junction in 1937. *W. L. Good*

Below left: No 5093 is climbing to Standish Junction, south of Gloucester, with the Down 'Devonian', while the fireman sits watching the road. *Real Photos 810*

Above: With a breath of steam only, Class 5 No 5096 approaches Wickwar Tunnel on a nine-coach Up express. *Real Photos 824*

Right: No 5050 is working easily in a Down semi-fast as she climbs past Yate in 1935. *Real Photos 583*

Below right: In the first flush of her youth, Class 5 No 5032, with original taller chimney and low-superheat boiler, drifts past Yate on an Up express. *Real Photos 555*

4

Prewar Performance

The second half of the 1930s, until the advent of World War 2, was a time of unrelenting pressure by the LMS operating authorities on locomotive performance. The effect of the slowly-improving national economy, and of keen competition with other railways and modes of travel, was such as to compel steady improvement in the speed of passenger train services, in the standards set by express freight trains in giving overnight transits, and in the general reliability and punctuality of both. These were the years of the 'On Time' campaign, with a monthly news-sheet of that name distributed at Motive Power Depots with details of new developments and outstanding performances — often rather crude, being compiled from a sifting of guards' journals — and punctuality competitions with awards of shields, etc. A great deal was done to stimulate enginemen's morale, as well as tightly monitoring the work of signalmen, station staff and others influencing timekeeping. Almost all aspects of train running were seen as a competitive challenge.

Into this world came the Stanier 4-6-0s, and they were immediately judged by the way in which they rose to that challenge. Until the proving process had been completed — and as recounted in the previous chapter it was to prove unexpectedly lengthy — there was of necessity some hesitation in train running circles in pushing acceleration too rapidly or too far. Only the 'Royal Scots' and, increasingly, the 'Princesses', inspired confidence for fast passenger work. In the case of the 'Jubilees', there were many furrowed brows until the sun began to break through in 1936.

As an example of what was happening at that time, let us look first at a Western Division run made with the first 'Jubilee' (later to become No 5642 in an exchange of identity) when only a few months old and carrying the original line 1 boiler and draughting.[29] The train was the Down 'Lakes Express' to Windermere and Keswick, with a 13-coach load (Table 6). At first sight things looked very fair. The fall from 64 to 59½ up the 1 in 339 past Hatch End, and then the maintenance of 60 over Tring, after half an hour of uninterrupted steaming, was in no way discreditable with this load, and the time of 33¾min to pass Tring was excellent. Equivalent DBHPs at Hatch End and Northchurch were about 1,100 and 1,160 respectively. But this could only have been achieved at some cost in pressure and (more so) water level. It is apparent that the engine coasted much of the way down to Bletchley — the average speed was only 65.5mph over these 15 miles — and the subsequent climbs to Roade and to Kilsby Tunnel show all the signs of the engine being 'winded'. But evidently the Rugby stop enabled the fireman to pull the boiler round, and onwards to Crewe the running was more consistent if less exciting, with about 880EDBHP being put out on the bank to Whitmore.

It is instructive to compare this performance with that of

Table 6
'Lakes Express' Euston-Windermere
Locomotive: Class 5XP 4-6-0 No 5552
Load: 13 coaches, 390 tons tare, 415 tons gross
Enginemen: Not recorded

Distance Miles		Special Limit Schedule minutes	Actual Time min sec	Speed
0.0	Euston	0	0.00	—
5.4	Willesden Jc	9	8.45	—
8.1	Wembley		11.11	64
13.2	Hatch End		16.26	59½ min
17.5	Watford Jc	22	20.24	70
24.5	Hemel Hempstead		26.47	—
28.0	Berkhamsted		30.10	—
31.7	Tring	38	33.44	60min
40.2	Leighton Buzzard		41.32	—
46.7	Bletchley	51	47.28	68
53.4	Wolverton		52.47	—
55.8	Castlethorpe		—	69
59.9	Roade	64	60.03	53
62.8	Blisworth	67	63.13	63
—	Kilsby Tunnel		—	47 min
			signals	
82.6	Rugby	88	85.55	
14.5	Nuneaton	16	16.20	75½
19.7	Atherstone		20.40	69
23.9	Polesworth		24.10	73
			pws	
27.4	Tamworth	29	27.42	65½ max
33.7	Lichfield	35	33.40	—
38.4	Armitage		38.24	57 min
41.7	Rugeley	43	41.20	67½
51.0	Stafford	53	50.40	*
56.3	Norton Bridge	60	56.55	—
60.8	Standon Bridge		—	60½
65.0	Whitmore	69	65.42	56 min
70.7	Betley Road		71.01	77½
		pass	signal stop	
75.5	Crewe	79	83.30	—

Net times: Euston-Rugby 85¼min
Rugby-Crewe 77min
*Permanent Speed Restriction

the pioneer Class 5, No 5020, in Table 5 with a load 78 tons heavier. The 'Jubilee' was faster out to Tring by 3½min, as might be expected, but on to Rugby the honours were unmistakably with the Class 5, which was 1min 50sec faster from Tring to Roade. From Rugby to Stafford the two engines were level pegging, with only 1sec between them, but the running of the 'Jubilee' from there to Whitmore was quite outdone by the smaller mixed traffic engine with two extra coaches.

While the Class 5s quickly settled down, the 'Jubilees' had much more to get right, and were slower to do so. One real

Table 7
Special Express, Coventry-Euston
Locomotive: Class 5XP 4-6-0 No 5552 *Silver Jubilee*
Load: 10 coaches, 331 tons tare, 345 tons gross
Enginemen: Dvr F. E. Smith, Fmn A. Arthurs (Camden)

Distance Miles		Schedule minutes	Actual Time min sec		Speed
0.0	Coventry	0	0.00		—
	Brandon Ballast Pit		pws		60/29
4.9	Brandon		7.41		—
11.4	Rugby	12	14.23		68/40*
18.7	Welton		22.01		62½
24.3	Weedon		26.25		80
31.2	Blisworth	30	31.51		75
34.1	Roade	33	34.07		72½
39.2	Castlethorpe		38.01		83
			signals		40
41.6	Wolverton		40.05		—
			signals		46
47.3	Bletchley	44	46.19		—
52.8	Leighton Buzzard		52.40		—
56.9	Cheddington		56.21		70
62.3	Tring	58	60.07		67
69.5	Hemel Hempstead		65.43		87
76.5	Watford Jc	70	70.36		88/83
80.8	Hatch End		73.45		78
85.8	Wembley		77.30		86
88.6	Willesden Jc	80	79.21		—
94.0	Euston	88	85.55		—

Net time: 83min
*Permanent Speed Restriction

difficulty on the straight throatplate boilers was firing over the hump in the grate, undoubtedly leading to some poor combustion conditions and/or excessive cooling air through an uneven fire, and it took firemen some time to get to know how to avoid this.

The advent of the line 2 boiler on engines Nos 5642-5646 brought about a first improvement in performance even while the draughting was still under development, and a run on a special express in 1935 with engine No 5552 *Silver Jubilee*[30] which had swapped identities with No 5642 in April 1935, shows that they *could* be made to sing in this form. Perhaps unusually, a Camden crew provided this little jewel set out in Table 7. Note the acceleration from the permanent 40mph (then) slack through Rugby to 62½ at Kilsby Tunnel South, the rushing of the Roade hump with no greater fall than from 75 to 72½, and the fine climb to Tring from the signal check at Loughton Siding. (How many times did we get that signal check approaching Bletchley!) The speeds down to Willesden, in the high 80s, were also fairly untypical of current Western Division standards. I calculate the EDBHP on the climb to Tring at about 1,170. But this last run was by no means typical of what was being done day-in, day-out by the new engines, and other published runs of this period showed few EDBHPs much above 800.

Elsewhere, the Class 5s had settled down to a very useful, if as yet unspectacular, working life. In considerable numbers they were allocated to all four Divisions, for both passenger and freight work. In Scotland, they largely took over the Highland lines south of Inverness from pre-grouping classes, and showed themselves capable of setting new standards under slogging conditions. For instance, C. J. Allen recorded a run behind No 5028, no doubt still with line 1 boiler, on a southbound train of 270 tons gross.[31] From the Newtonmore restart:

'After being checked at 15mph for relaying at Inchlea Crossing, this engine worked up to 44mph before Dalwhinnie, notwithstanding . . . that the only respite in 2¾ miles of 1 in 100 up is ⅜-mile of level in the centre of it. Even on the final 1 in 100 speed did not fall below 40mph. . . . From Dalwhinnie start, up 2¾ miles of 1 in 80, speed rose to 32mph; the easier strip, mostly at 1 in 100, raised it to 39½, and the final mile of 1 in 80 (to Druimuachdar Summit) reduced it to 36mph.'

I calculate the EDBHP at mp 55¾ at about 1,050 at 32mph.

In the last months of 1936, after I had started my engineering apprenticeship in the Locomotive Works at Derby, considerable numbers of the No 5225-5451 Armstrong Whitworth engines were allocated to the Midland Division, and immediately became a force to be reckoned with, notably on the St Pancras-Manchester Central trains, where at that time they had a virtual monopoly because bridge restrictions through the Peak District barred the 'Jubilees'. Typical of the hardest Class 5 jobs was the 16.30 Manchester-St Pancras; when the author was going home on a Friday night in 1937 the eight-coach train arriving at Derby was invariably made up to 10 or 11 coaches *plus* four, five or even six 3,000-gallon six-wheeled milk tanks from Staffordshire and Derbyshire creameries. These tanks, loaded, each weighed over 25 tons, so that the Class 5 was expected to — and did — take a train of 470-495 tons to London on 'Special Limit' timings, usually without assistance. Out of Derby at 18.04 and calling at Loughborough, Leicester and Luton, it was into St Pancras at 20.30.

So successful were the Class 5s on the Highland main line services that accelerations were in the operators' minds. In January 1937 a little-publicised series of dynamometer car trials was conducted to see whether these would be feasible, and it proved to be a revealing fortnight. The engine used was No 5159, fitted with line 5 straight throatplate boiler. A complex programme on a wide spectrum of trains took the engine from Inverness to Perth and to Wick, with various intermediate workings — a fair cross-section of Highland line work. Loads varied from 252 to 369 tons. The weather was wintry, with some snow. Douglas Castle coal, a Lanarkshire Grade 1, was burned throughout.

Dynamometer Car Report No 68 ' . . . considered that the engine was well handled throughout', as might be expected from men brought up on a hard road. 'The steaming of the engine was good' — no pressure below 210lb/sq in being recorded — 'but this was only attained when working at late cutoffs by very careful operation of the exhaust steam injector, and a point was made of filling the boiler at each stop'. In other words, the fireman was mortgaging the boiler during hard working and recouping during the station stops. 'It was possible to operate the water control regulator of the exhaust injector so that the water level . . . was never less than half full when working under the above conditions'. Lucky fireman!

In most cases sectional timings were well kept, but now and then the enginemen were called upon to do the impossible. On the first day, working the 08.25 Inverness-Perth express with 255 tons, 'sectional timekeeping Inverness to Slochd was not maintained, although the engine was worked continuously at ... 35-45% with full regulator', only sustaining 25mph on the 1 in 60 banks with no higher DBHP than 765 above Tomatin. Now this was not hard working as Inverness men understood the term; but that afternoon, No 5159 had to run the 16.00 Perth-Blair Atholl *stopping* train made up to no less than 369 tons behind the tender (why this load for a rural stopping train is not apparent!). Sectional time could not be maintained with this load. On three occasions the engine had to reverse before a start could be made on rising grades. From Stanley Junction to the top of the bank before Murthly, at 1 in 80/93, for instance, 55% cutoff with full regulator had to be used, though on the easier grades 30% sufficed. On 20 January, working the 16.50 Blair Atholl-Perth with the same load, sectional times were 'in general maintained without difficulty, due to the ruling falling gradients'. On the one nasty climb, from Dunkeld to Kingswood Crossing, 2.6 miles mainly at 1 in 80, the 6min schedule was improved on by $\frac{1}{4}$min, 45-50% cutoff producing a maximum of 1,080DBHP at 30mph. On the other workings time-keeping was good.

The consumption figures give another indication of the hard slogging involved on these Highland trains with severe grades and frequent stops or slowings for loops. I have omitted those for 26 January (Inverness-Aviemore and back) and 28/29 January (Inverness-Helmsdale and back) for the sake of brevity, but the remainder are reproduced below, grouped by route and type of train.

From observations of water consumption over selected severe sections, it was calculated that combustion rates under these conditions were reaching figures of the order of 120lb/ sq ft of grate/hr. Not surprisingly, therefore, the conclusion drawn from the tests was that:

'While in general the timekeeping and the steaming of the engine was satisfactory, the results indicate that the test workings involved the engine being operated beyond the point where economy is secured, and therefore an acceleration with the loads of the test could not be recommended. If it is desired to reduce the present scheduled timings, it will be necessary for the booked loads of these trains to be reduced to, say, 150-200 tons.'

on the Midland Division became paramount, and given the conclusions of the report on the trials with No 5740, the Operating Department called for an assessment of the capabilities of the 'Jubilees' on the routes from St Pancras to Leeds and of Class 5s to Manchester Central against proposed timings — in due course to be the basis of the 'XL Limit' timings — for the Winter 1937 timetable. Compared with the current best 'Special Limit' times, these represented an acceleration of about 10min between St Pancras and Leicester, and St Pancras and Nottingham.

Engine No 5614, recently returned from Crewe works to Kentish Town modified with a line 15 sloping throatplate boiler, was selected to make the Leeds runs on 20 and 21 April 1937; on 22 April, Class 5 No 5278 (line 8 boiler) was used for the Manchester train and No 5264 for the return trip. The loadings of the special trains was 302 tons for the 'Jubilee' and 258 tons for the Class 5. Grimethorpe Grade 1 coal was used except on No 5264, where because of a last-minute substitution she was coaled with another Grade 1, Dalton Main.

Dynamometer Car Report No 70 notes that the steaming of No 5614 was 'completely satisfactory throughout'. With No 5278:

' ... the steaming was poor to Leicester, due to developed defects, and as a result the engine failed to maintain sectional running times over this section. Subsequently there was an improvement in the engine's steaming ... between Leicester and Manchester'.

However, after examination at Trafford Park shed, it was decided to replace No 5278 by a similar engine, No 5264, which was just a month older. With no special preparation to make the test run, the surrogate Class 5 'steamed very well throughout'.

The timings which the engines were expected to keep were distinctly tight — 96min each way between St Pancras and Leicester (99.1 miles) and $118\frac{1}{2}$min St Pancras-Nottingham and 120min return (123.5 miles). But so frequent were permanent way slacks and (sad to say) the odd signal check in the Erewash Valley and further north, and thus so poor the

	Inverness-Perth				Perth-Blair Atholl	Inverness-Wick
	19 Jan Up Express	22 Jan Down Express	20 Jan Down Stopping	21 Jan Up Stopping	19/29 Jan Dn & Up Stopping	27 Jan Dn & Up Stopping*
Load, tons	255	256/254	258/255	255/262	369	298/302
Speeds, average	40.9	37.4	34.4	34.3	30.2	33.6
max	64	58	60	67	38	56
Coal: lb/mile	66.5	51.7	54.6	59.2	80.2	52.5
lb/DBHP hr	5.19	4.80	4.09	4.80	4.48	4.19
lb/sq ft/hr	98.0	69.6	67.5	73.1	86.8	63.5
Water: gal/mile	37.9	32.0	36.9	36.8	55.8	37.9
lb/DBHP hr	29.6	29.7	27.7	29.8	31.2	30.2
Evaporation: lb/lb coal	5.71	6.20	6.76	6.22	6.97	7.22

*Up train express from Tain

A suggestion which was obvious anathema to the Operating Department.

By now the operators and enginemen had total confidence in the Class 5s, straight and sloping throatplate engines alike. Furthermore, the dynamometer car tests with the later 'Jubilees', backed by a crash programme of boiler and draughting modifications, was bringing fair confidence there, too. Now the commercial pressures for further acceleration

timekeeping, that the running north of Leicester and Nottingham has been ignored. Within this compass the report confirms that sectional time-keeping was ' ... with two exceptions very satisfactory ... ' The first of these exceptions was a sheer impossibility to achieve — 6.9 miles from a cold start at St Pancras to Hendon in 9min, of which the first $4\frac{1}{2}$ miles were hard uphill slog, much at 1 in 176/178. No 5614 took 11min 5sec and 10min 30sec, while No 5278 managed

10min 20sec. The second exception, 6min for 4.8 miles from Desborough to Market Harborough, mainly at 1 in 133/132 down, was not difficult, but for No 5614 to take 6min 45sec suggests some out-of-course check which went unrecorded; even the poor-steaming No 5278, no doubt mainly coasting, took only 6min 20sec.

Much more information is now available than in 1937 to enable locomotive performance to be calculated. So, in setting out details of the test running in Tables 8-11, particulars of the calculated running for a similar engine, the BR Standard Class 5, on a 305ton train and steaming at a steady water rate of 18,000lb/hr using the exhaust steam injector, have been included between St Pancras and Leicester as a datum.[32] Because of the steaming problems the running of No 5278 has been omitted. The timings shown are a mixture of those recorded in the dynamometer car or as published by the late C. J. Allen, as appropriate.[33] The Up timings from Nottingham are dynamometer car figures because those published by Allen show a discrepancy of about +20sec from Luton inwards which are not consistent with the recorded speeds. In one case speeds have had to be averaged from the official timings, but otherwise are as recorded by independent observers and published by Allen.

In comparing the test performances with the calculated times and speeds, it should be borne in mind that few drivers on a route with the Midland's saw-tooth profile would drive at a constant steam rate, which gives high downhill and relatively low uphill speeds. They would normally work harder uphill, mortgaging the boiler water level to some extent, recouping this on the downhill lengths ready for the next climb, a technique giving the best running times for a given coal consumption. On the run to Leicester (Table 8), for instance, the Kentish Town crew, while running very closely to the calculated overall times as far as Bedford, were 40sec faster from Hendon to St Albans and 38sec faster up to Sharnbrook Summit (mp $59\frac{3}{4}$). On the following day Driver Howard made an even finer start out to St Albans, and could then afford to run more easily to Bedford. Fireman Hall must have put in some very careful work in preparing his fire to sustain this effort right from the start. The speeds of 61 at Sandridge and $53\frac{1}{2}$ at mp $59\frac{3}{4}$ were excellent; actual DBHPs were 950 and 1,010 respectively, so that the EDBHPs must have been about 1,180 and 1,250 at these points. Howard's acceleration from the slack over Melton Junction up 1 in 200 at 56 at the summit beyond Grimston involved power rising to a peak of 1,130DBHP, equivalent to

Table 8

Dynamometer Car Test Runs: St Pancras-Leeds 1937

Date:		—			20 April			21 April	
Locomotive:		BR Std Class 5 4-6-0‡			Class 5XP 4-6-0 No 5614			Class 5XP 4-6-0 No 5614	
Load: coaches:		—			9			9	
tons tare/gross		305/330			302/305			302/305	
Enginemen		—			Not recorded			Dvr Howard, Fmn Hall	

Distance Miles		XL Limit Schedule Minutes	Calculated Time Min Sec	Speed	Test Schedule Minutes	Actual Time Min Sec	Average Speed	Actual Time Min Sec	Speed
0.0	St Pancras	0	0.00	—	0	0.00	—	0.00	—
1.5	Kentish Town	4	3.36	42	4	3.45	—	3.41	$37\frac{1}{2}$
6.9	Hendon	$10\frac{1}{2}$	11.00	$48/64\frac{1}{2}$	9	11.05	44.2	10.30	65
12.4	Elstree		17.10	$54\frac{1}{2}/57/51$		—		16.05	56
15.2	Radlett		19.21	$80\frac{1}{2}$		—		18.33	75
19.9	St Albans	23	23.13	55min	22	23.25	63.3	22.37	61min
24.6	Harpenden		27.49	$73/66\frac{1}{2}/79$		—		27.09	69/75
30.2	Luton	33	32.25	$66\frac{1}{2}/75$	31	32.15	70.0	31.51	72/75
37.3	Harlington		38.08	67/88		—		37.24	82
41.8	Ampthill		—	$90*/86\frac{1}{2}$		—		40.40	$85/80\frac{1}{2}$
49.8	Bedford	49	46.34	$90*/85/89$	$46\frac{1}{2}$	46.25	83.0	46.23	$86/83\frac{1}{2}$
53.0	Oakley		48.55	72/79		—		48.51	73
59.8	mp $59\frac{3}{4}$	$58\frac{1}{2}$	55.32	$42\frac{1}{2}$min	56	54.45	72.0	55.11	$53\frac{1}{2}$min
65.0	Wellingborough	$63\frac{1}{2}$	60.10	78/65*	$60\frac{1}{2}$	59.10	70.6	59.45	79/56*
68.2	Finedon	—		71/68$\frac{1}{2}$				62.46	67
72.0	Kettering	70	66.17	$72/60\frac{1}{2}$	67	65.45	63.8	66.23	20*
78.1	Desborough		73.41†	$46/58\frac{1}{2}/46$	74	72.00	58.6		
82.9	Market Harboro'	82	77.38	$82/50*/71$	79	78.45	42.7		
89.4	Kibworth North		84.43	$50/75/71\frac{1}{2}$	—				
99.1	Leicester	99	94.34	$82\frac{1}{2}/40*$	96	95.45	57.2		
79.5	Corby							76.11	60/70
90.1	Manton				86			85.39	75/61/64
93.8	Oakham							89.19	$58\frac{1}{2}$
101.5	Saxby							96.06	$76\frac{1}{2}$
105.3	Melton Mowbray				100			99.22	46*
109.2	Grimston							104.01	54
118.1	Plumtree							111.30	$69/87\frac{1}{2}$
123.5	Nottingham				$118\frac{1}{2}$			117.10	—

*Permanent speed restriction

†Desborough North box (78.5 miles)

‡Working at 18,000lb/hr water rate with exhaust steam injector (19,150lb/hr steam) except for first 10min from start at 16,000lb/hr water rate

Table 9

Dynamometer Car Test Run: Manchester (Central)–St Pancras, 22 April 1937.

Locomotive: Class 5MT 4-6-0 No 5264
Load: Coaches 8
      tons tare/gross 258/260
Enginemen: Dvr Beebe, Fmn Foulkes.

Distance miles		Test Schedule minutes	Actual Time min sec	Speed
0.0	Manchester (Central)	0	0.00	—
1.5	Throstle Nest South Jc		3.37	*
3.2	Chorlton	6	6.03	53
5.7	Didsbury		8.36	68/64
8.0	Cheadle Heath	11	10.37	68
9.5	Top of 1 in 100		—	57½
10.7	Top of 1 in 140		—	59
12.0	Hazel Grove		14.38	57
15.2	Disley		18.13	54/59
17.0	New Mills South Jc	22½	20.07	55
19.7	Chinley	26½	23.40	43
21.7	Chapel-en-le-Frith		26.36	38
25.4	Peak Forest	35½	32.57	34min
28.2	Peak Forest Jc		35.45	35*
30.0	Millers Dale	40½	38.23	56
32.7	Monsal Dale		41.00	66/60
36.4	Bakewell		44.39	66/63
39.8	Rowsley	50½	48.00	35*
44.2	Matlock		52.53	67/45*
51.0	Ambergate	62½	61.45	45*/17*
58.1	Little Eaton Jc		69.15	77½
61.4	Derby	73	73.10	—

*Permanent Speed Restriction

---

about 1,310EDBHP, and sustained at over 950DBHP as far as Widmerpool, a total of about nine miles.

In the Up direction the work of North and George was a little erratic on the Leicester day (Table 10). The initial start — the train must have been over 10min late — was somewhat slower than the calculated times, and there was some heavy-handedness with the brake for the Wigston and Market Harborough slacks, but the engine was put fairly hard at the 1 in 133 to Desborough North to make a steady 44, the calculated EDBHP being 1,070. The climb to Sharnbrook Summit was ruined by a permanent way slack, but having lost time from Leicester, some energetic running was made from Bedford, with an EDBHP above Harlington of over 1,200. The last stage from Sundon to mp 34 showed some easement, perhaps for falling water level, for the summit was passed at 63 as against a calculated 51, implying a steam rate well above the reference figure.

The work of Driver Beebe on No 5264 on 22 April was rather different; in the early stages from Leicester he left No 5614 standing, and bettered the calculated time to Desborough North by over a minute. The getaways were faster, though the braking for Wigston and Market Harborough were every bit as rough as that of George, and the climb to Kibworth North (1½ miles of 1 in 156/161 with no greater loss of speed than from 67 to 65 — about 1,320EDBHP) and to Desborough North (4½ miles of 1 in 132/133 on which he accelerated to 56 — about 1,300EDBHP) were magnificent. But the long pull from Bedford up to mp 34 was taken rather more sedately, perhaps to avoid undue gain on schedule, the Bedford-Luton time being 18min 5sec as against No 5614's

---

Table 10

Dynamometer Car Test Runs: Leeds-St Pancras 1937

Date		—			20 April			22 April	
Locomotive:		BR Std Class 5 4-6-0†			Class 5XP 4-6-0 No 5614			Class 5MT 4-6-0 No 5264	
Load: coaches		—			9			8	
tons tare/gross		305/330			302/305			258/260	
Enginemen		—			Dr North, Fmn George			Dr Beebe, Fmn Foulkes	
Distance Miles		XL Limit Schedule Minutes	Calculated Time Min Sec	Speed	Test Schedule Minutes	Actual Time Min Sec	Speed	Actual Time Min Sec	Speed
0.0	Leicester	0	0.00	—	0	0.00	—	0.00	—
3.2	Wigston North Jc		4.53	53/40*		5.27	50/35*	5.15	52/30*
9.3	Kibworth North		11.54	56/53/61/52½		12.30	63/58	11.58	67/65
16.1	Market Harborough	19	17.39	86½/50*	18	18.26	82/43*	17.15	86½/43*
20.6	Desborough North		23.39	41		24.17	44	22.33	56
27.1	Kettering	31	28.58	85/70*	29	30.00	78/71*	28.05	77½/66*
34.0	Wellingborough	37	34.41	81½/65*	35	35.29	80½/65*	33.40	79/61*
							pws 67/23	pws	69/23
39.3	mp 59¾	43	40.34	67/42	40½	41.54	27	39.44	30
46.1	Oakley		45.48	90*/87½		48.00	84/75‡	45.38	86½/66‡
49.3	Bedford	51	48.07	89/79/86	48½	50.26	83½	48.12	85
57.3	Ampthill		55.03	78/81/55½		56.49	67	55.05	55
61.8	Harlington		59.43	60½/54		60.43	69	59.35	63/60
65.1	mp 34		—	51		63.45	63	62.52	59
68.9	Luton	70	67.10	66½/79½	68	66.59	66½/74	66.17	74/67
74.5	Harpenden		71.47	79½/69		71.23	80½/73	71.10	73/65
79.2	St Albans	79	75.41	77½/71/75*	76½	75.10	75	75.30	—
83.9	Radlett		79.09	86		78.35	87	79.25	78
86.6	Elstree		81.12	66		80.42	76½	81.36	70
92.1	Hendon	90	85.33	90*	87	84.42	86	85.33	91
97.6	Kentish Town	96	89.53	65*	93	89.44	—	89.53	—
99.1	St Pancras	99	93.22	—	96	92.28		92.36	

*Permanent Speed Restriction
†Working at 18,000lb/hr water rate with exhaust steam injector (19,150lb/hr steam)
‡Reduced for taking water on Oakley troughs
Net times: No 5614, 90½min, No 5264, 91¼min

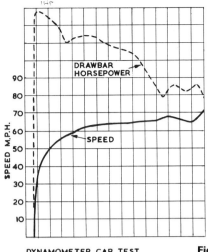

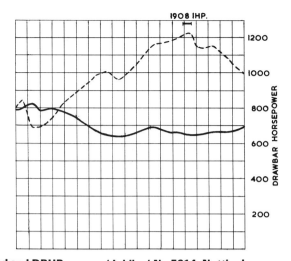

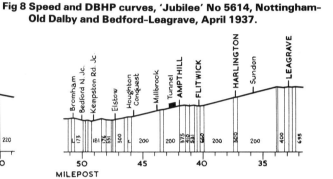

DYNAMOMETER CAR TEST
21 APRIL 1937
CLASS 5XP 4-6-0 5614
LOAD 302 TONS

NOTTINGHAM · EDWALTON · PLUMTREE · Stanton Tunnel · WIDMERPOOL · UPPER BROUGHTON · OLD DALBY · Grimston Tunnel

330 L 200 L 220 L 200 400 264 200 264 220 220

120   115   110

Fig 8 Speed and DBHP curves, 'Jubilee' No 5614, Nottingham-Old Dalby and Bedford-Leagrave, April 1937.

Bromham · Bedford N. Jc. · Kempston Rd. Jc. · Elstow · Houghton Conquest · Millbrook · Tunnel · AMPTHILL · FLITWICK · HARLINGTON · Sundon · LEAGRAVE

175 181 176 351 300 L 200 575 410 551 660 200 300 200 400 695

50   45   40   35

MILEPOST

16min 33sec and a calculated 19min 3sec. Even so, the sustained 59 on the final 1 in 200 reflected a power output of 1,025EDBHP. After this the first recorded 90 plus for a Class 5 showed that 180 miles of arduous running had not taken too great a toll of engine or crew. The net time of 91¼min certainly indicated scope for acceleration with a margin for recovery with this load.

The work of North and George on 21 April from Nottingham (Table 11) surpassed their previous day's performance. A remarkable start was made up the 1 in 200 to Widmerpool, with speed worked up to 64 (Fig 8). Actual DBHP was over 1,100 throughout this climb, with a peak of 1,280, and the average EDBHP must have been a little over 1,300, though no doubt achieved at some expense in water level. The running down from Manton to Harringworth was very restrained by normal standards, but once on the main line at Kettering Junction any inhibitions were quickly left behind and the climb to mp 59¾ was outstanding. The fall in speed from 66 to 64½ up 3½ miles of 1 in 202 from Harlington, after 15min of hard steaming, was a major effort; actual DBHPs were over 1,000 from Ampthill to beyond Leagrave, peaking at 1,200 above Harlington, the corresponding EDBHPs being about 220 higher. From Luton inwards, speeds were high but by no means at record levels. Fig 8 also shows speeds and power output on the climb from Bedford.

Lastly, a word about the Derby-Manchester section. On the Down train, the steaming of No 5278 improved immensely after Leicester, and the report comments that '... from Derby to Peak Forest ... where the demand on the engine was exceptional, timekeeping was excellent'. It was, indeed. From Rowsley to Peak Forest, 14.4 miles of long 1 in 100 banks culminating in 3 miles of 1 in 90 and started from a 45mph restriction over Rowsley curve, for which 20min was allowed, Nos 5278 lifted her train in 18min 35sec, sustaining 47-49 continuously on the 1 in 100 and producing

Table 11

Dynamometer Car Test Run: Leeds-St Pancras, 21 April 1937

Locomotive: Class 5XP 4-6-0 No 5614
Load: coaches 9
 tons tare/gross 302/305
Enginemen: Dvr North, Fmn George (Holbeck)

Distance miles		Test Schedule minutes	Actual Time min sec	Speed
0.0	Nottingham	0	0.00	—
2.8	Edwalton		—	56
8.3	Widmerpool		—	64
10.9	Upper Broughton		—	70/65
18.2	Melton Mowbray	21	18.40	77½/47*
22.0	Saxby		—	63
29.7	Oakham		—	70
33.4	Manton	35	32.35	73
44.0	Corby		—	72/58
51.5	Kettering	52	49.45	74/64/67
52.8	Kettering Jc	54	51.30	20*
58.4	Wellingborough	59	57.25	68/60*
			pws	67/21
63.7	mp 59¾	64½	64.00	26
70.5	Oakley		—	83½/76½†
73.7	Bedford	72½	72.10	83½
81.7	Ampthill		—	63/71
86.2	Harlington		—	66
89.5	mp 34		—	64½
93.3	Luton	92	89.10	82/77½
98.9	Harpenden		—	82/77½
103.6	St Albans	100½	96.55	73
108.3	Radlett		—	84
110.0	Elstree		—	74
116.5	Hendon	111	106.40	85
122.0	Kentish Town	117	111.35	59*
123.5	St Pancras	120	114.30	—

Net Time 113min
†Reduced for taking water on Oakley Troughs
*Permanent Speed Restriction

about 1,310EDBHP. Her recovery from earlier troubles was convincing.

On the return journey, No 5264 did some spectacular work from Cheadle Heath up to Chinley, even though the average speed does not quite support the speed of 54 quoted in Table 9 at the south end of Disley Tunnel; perhaps 52 would have been nearer the mark at this point. Up to Hazel Grove No 5264 was producing about 1,350EDBHP, but the fall in speed through Disley Tunnel probably resulted from deliberate easing to avoid slipping in the tunnel. Similarly, the minimum of 34 at Peak Forest almost certainly reflected some easing, for Dove Holes Tunnel (what a misnomer!) was a filthy wet hole, and very ready to cause a slip. The EDBHP there was only about 950. Once over the top, the running was governed by speed restrictions for curvature as far as Ambergate, and C. J. Allen spoke of 'exaggerated . . . attention paid to curves between Rowsley and Ambergate', where $1\frac{3}{4}$min was dropped and speed only averaged 48.9mph. There was a bright sprint from the Ambergate station slack into Derby.

The report is somewhat uncommunicative about the working of the engines, contenting itself with saying that on 21 April (No 5614) 30% cutoff was used on the level and easier grades — much harder than was usual on the Euston-Birmingham line — and that on the climb out of Sheffield to Dore & Totley, at 1 in 100, a sustained cutoff of 45% was used, which produced a steady $42\frac{1}{2}$mph with 1,140DBHP. This would have equated to about 1,440EDBHP. It is probable that up to mp 34 about 35% cutoff was in force. However the report does comment that:

'While the steaming of the engines was maintained, the conditions of the run (timings and permanent way restrictions) involved the high average combustion rate of 100lb/sq ft of grate/hr and was, therefore, *beyond the range of operation which is attended with economy.*'

The italics are mine, for this was a profound remark; if the writer of the report had added (justifiably) the words 'and reliability', perhaps more notice might with advantage have been taken in later years.

Because of the engine change at Trafford Park, coal and water consumption figures for the Class 5 could not, unfortunately, be produced, but it might be expected that the coal figure would have been about 3.6lb/DBHP hr. The corresponding figures for No 5614 were fairly eye-opening by comparison with Western Division tests, and clearly showed the arduous nature of what was planned, quite apart from the cost of the exceptional efforts made on second day:

	20 April	*21 April*
Work Done: HP hrs	4527	5450
Coal: lb/mile	45.3	55.4
lb/DBHP hr	3.93	4.13
lb/sq ft/hr	84.0	100.5
Water: gal/mile	33.1*	34.7
lb/DBHP hr	28.8*	25.9
Evaporation: lb/lb coal	7.30*	6.28

*unreliable, due to fractured feed pipe wasting water.

The report concluded that:

'. . . The actual time schedule in conjunction with a loading of the test required a high power development, and at some points the maximum which could be expected from the engines . . . In this respect the 5X and the Class 5 were completely satisfactory, and the steaming of both engines well maintained. . . . a modification of these conditions would be necessary for the laying down of an accelerated service . . .'

While the CME staff were clearly proud of what the two engines had achieved, the wording suggests an attempt to inject a note of caution to curb any over-enthusiasm on the part of the operators, but this was only partially successful. At a subsequent inter-departmental meeting, some easement of running times was agreed, the revised ones being 'practically in accordance with the speed and power curves which have been calculated for the engines'. (This is believed to refer to curves published by Stanier in 1938.)[34] These timings allowed 99min to and from Leicester (instead of 96) and 123min to and from Nottingham (instead of $118\frac{1}{2}$ Down and 120 Up). Such was the manner in which the Midland mile-a-minute service at last dawned late in 1937.

The quite excellent work done by Nos 5614 and 5264 was, of course, under test conditions, but work of comparable standard was by this time being done in normal daily running, and not all in the most expected places. Take the old Central Division of the LMS, for instance, straddling the Pennines from the Lancashire Coast to Leeds and Goole. The Central's allocation of 'Jubilees' was always limited, never reaching as many as 30, and inevitably plenty of express running fell to be handled by Class 5s, duties which they fulfilled admirably, as the following run will confirm. This was over a hard but unspectacular route which very rarely figured in any published train running analysis, the ex-LNWR line between Manchester and Leeds via Huddersfield. There the interest centres on the climb from Stalybridge, hampered by a severe speed restriction through the station into the tunnel, up to Diggle and the wet and (then) foul Standedge Tunnel; seven punishing miles at 1 in 125/151/125/175/125, the average being 1 in 136, on a sinuous course up the valley.

The engine was No 5363, and would probably have been in the hands of Edge Hill men. Table 12[35] shows that the Stalybridge slack was taken in slightly cavalier fashion, but to

Table 12

09.00 Liverpool Lime St-Newcastle
Locomotive: Class 5MT 4-6-0 No 5363
Load: coaches 9
        tons tare/gross: 293/310
Enginemen: Not recorded

Distance miles		Schedule minutes	Actual Time min sec	Speed
0.0	Manchester Ex	0	0.00	†
8.1	Stalybridge	14	13.23	30*
10.7	Mossley		18.05	44
				on 1 in 125
12.8	Greenfield	21	20.55	47
				on 1 in 150
14.0	Saddleworth		22.18	52
				on 1 in 175
15.3	Diggle	24	23.47	51
				on 1 in 125
18.9	Marsden	29	27.50	45*
21.5	Slaithwaite		30.25	66
			signals	
26.0	Huddersfield	38	36.32	—

†Banked in rear to Miles Platting
*Permanent Speed Restrictions

45

lift her nine-coach train the engine was put at the bank very hard, and appeared able to sustain 49mph on 1 in 125 without difficulty — requiring about 1,350EDBHP — for 10min or so. The continuation from Huddersfield was over the Heckmondwike loop, a viciously graded and tortuous route now disappeared, and C. J. Allen commented at the time 'the impressive feature of this run was the effortless competence with which the engine attacked these banks'. Perhaps he was sitting at the rear of the train, for while not denying the competence, the effort must have been fairly noisy!

Enginemen system-wide were also getting the measure of the 'Jubilees' as the draughting was modified and higher superheat provided. On the old Caledonian main line over Beattock, some really excellent work was recorded in 1938 with No 5636,[36] by this time carrying a 24-element superheater boiler (Table 3, line 9). As will be seen from Table 13, even time was achieved before Ecclefechan and the climb from Beattock to the summit, 10.0 miles, made in the fast time of 13min 58sec. Note the sustained 68½ up the 1 in 200 from Ecclefechan to Castlemilk summit, and the acceleration on the final stages of Beattock bank, from 33½ to 35½ on 1 in 74/77. The calculated EDBHP's were about 1,220 and 1,160 respectively.

Table 13

Carlisle-Edinburgh Princes Street

Locomotive: Class 5XP 4-6-0 No 5636 *Uganda*
Load: 8 coaches, 231 tons tare, 245 tons gross
Enginemen: Not recorded

Distance miles		Schedule minutes	Actual Time min sec	Speed
0.0	Carlisle	0	0.00	—
4.1	Rockcliffe		5.45	65
6.1	Floriston		7.32	79 max
8.6	Gretna	10	9.31	69½
13.0	Kirkpatrick		13.34	61 min
16.7	Kirtlebridge		16.58	76
20.1	Ecclefechan		19.51	68½
22.7	Castlemilk Siding		22.08	68½
25.8	Lockerbie	28	24.39	79 max
31.8	Dinwoodie		29.22	68½
34.5	Wamphray		31.40	74½
39.7	Beattock	40	36.10	66
42.2	Auchencastle		38.43	51
45.3	Greskine		42.50	40
47.7	Harthope		46.40	33½
49.7	Beattock Summit	57	50.08	35½
73.2	Strawfrank Jc	80	70.33	31½*
90.5	Midcalder	102	88.52	57* eased
100.6	Edinburgh Princes Street	116	104.15	—

*Permanent Speed Restriction

At the same time, on the Midland main line, similar climbing was being combined with demonstrations of the 'Jubilees'' ability to run fast. Table 14 sets out a quite remarkable run[37] on the 99min timing from Leicester to St Pancras with a light 7-coach train. The engine at this time (early 1938) must have been nearly ready for shopping, and was still fitted with her straight throatplate boiler, though by now with a 24-element superheater (Table 3, line 9). Observe the minimum of 63 over the hump at Kibworth North, the attained 60 up the 1 in 133 to Desborough North (at least 1,330EDBHP), 56 virtually sustained up the 1 in 120 to mp 59¾ (1,260EDBHP) and the remarkable minimum of 71 up the 1 in 200 to mp 34 (1,200EDBHP). And in between these efforts, 89 before

Table 14

Leicester-St Pancras

Locomotive: Class 5XP 4-6-0 No 5622 *Nyasaland*
Load: 7 coaches, 225 tons tare, 235 tons gross
Enginemen: Not recorded

Distance Miles		Schedule Minutes	Actual Time Min Sec	Speed
0.0	Leicester	0	0.00	—
			pws	15
3.7	Wigston		9.04	—
7.5	Great Glen		14.00	65
9.4	Kibworth North		15.38	63
12.8	East Langton		18.11	89
16.2	Market Harborough	19	21.00	38*
20.6	Desborough North		26.04	60
27.1	Kettering	31	30.51	93/82*
30.8	Finedon		33.33	89
			signals	5
34.1	Wellingborough	37	40.30	—
36.4	Irchester		43.25	57
39.3	mp 59¾	43	46.29	56
46.1	Oakley		51.33	93/82
49.3	Bedford	51	53.50	87
57.3	Ampthill		59.51	72
58.9	Flitwick		61.09	77
61.8	Harlington		63.30	73
66.3	Leagrave		67.14	71
68.9	Luton	70	69.11	84
74.5	Harpenden		73.20	86/78
79.2	St Albans	79	76.54	86
83.9	Radlett		80.01	95
86.7	Elstree		82.00	76
92.1	Hendon	90	85.46	91
97.6	Kentish Town	96	90.34	—
			signals	
99.1	St Pancras	99	96.10	—

*Permanent Speed Restriction
Net Time: 84½min

Market Harborough, 93 before and 89 after Kettering, 93 at Oakley, 95 at Radlett and 91 at Hendon, all of which would require some steady steaming. No lack of confidence of men in their machine here! Perhaps it might have been better if they had been a shade less exuberant, for some of the speeds show scant respect for speed limits — 82 instead of 70 through Kettering, 84-86 through the 75mph curves south of Luton, and 86 through St Albans instead of 75.

These two 'Jubilee' runs exemplify the sort of work for which these engines were ideally fitted — trains of about 250 tons on a line with scope for fast running and with climbs not exceeding about 15 minutes at a time. Under such conditions they produced sparkling performances, whereas on trains in excess of 300 tons, especially where lengthy hard running was needed, they required the most expert handling by both driver and fireman working as a team; unfortunately, such teamwork was not always forthcoming.

Which brings us to one of the finest examples of footplate teamwork that was ever seen on the LMS. The second phase of the Midland acceleration was in preparation, embracing the Derby-Bristol route and the Leeds-Carlisle-Glasgow service via the 'Long Drag' and the G&SW line. Special dynamometer car test trains were run on 12-15 October 1937, the first day covering Bristol-Leeds with stops at Gloucester, Cheltenham, Birmingham, Derby and Sheffield (plus Bromsgrove for banking engine), and on the second day Leeds-Glasgow stopping at Carlisle, Annan, Dumfries and Kilmarnock. The return was made in the same way with the same stops except for the regulation brake stop at Blackwell instead of Bromsgrove. The engine selected was No 5660 *Rooke*, which had run nearly 12,000 miles since General Repair in July, at which a line 15 sloping throatplate boiler had been fitted.

An unusual feature of the Special Train Notice issued for these runs, by modern standards, was that the train crews were specified by name, the enginemen being:

Bristol-Leeds and return: Driver E. Gardner, Fireman P. R. Hook (Bristol).
Leeds-Glasgow and return: Driver W. North, Fireman H. George (Holbeck).

The timings postulated were very difficult in view of the nature of the road:

	Miles	Northbound		Southbound	
		min	Av speed	min	Av speed
Bristol-Gloucester	37.0	38	58.4	39	56.9
Gloucester-Cheltenham	6.5	10	39.0	10	39.0
Cheltenham-Birmingham	45.5	51	53.5	50	54.6
Birmingham-Derby	41.2	41	60.4	41	60.4
Derby-Sheffield	36.4	42	52.0	41½	52.6
Sheffield-Leeds	39.5	46	51.5	46½	51.0
Leeds-Carlisle	113.0	117	57.9	125	54.2
Carlisle-Annan	17.6	18	58.7	19	55.6
Annan-Dumfries	15.5	15½	60.0	16	58.1
Dumfries-Kilmarnock	58.0	62	56.1	62	56.1
Kilmarnock-Glasgow	24.4	29½	49.6	31	47.2
Overall	434.6	471	55.4	481	54.2

The Notice also laid down the following blanket speed limits:

Between Bristol and Gloucester   80mph
Between Gloucester and Birmingham   85mph
Between Birmingham and Derby   90mph
Between Derby and Glasgow   80mph

There were, in addition, numerous relaxations of local restrictions, etc.

Dynamometer Car Report No 72 shows just how hard *Rooke* had to be worked to meet these schedules. The general cutoff on the level and easier gradients was 25-30%, but on the heavier grades 35% was the norm and 40% not uncommon, with occasional instances of 45% and above, mainly for difficult starts from such stations as Sheffield and Birmingham. The Report says that:

'The steaming of the engine was completely satisfactory. It was possible to maintain a good level of water in the boiler when working under the most severe conditions.'

To demonstrate the quality of the running, it is tempting to tabulate complete details, but lack of space brings a need for selectivity. With the exception of the Glasgow-Leeds journey, where the more detailed timings published by C. J. Allen have been used,[38] never more than 8sec different from the official record, any times are as recorded in the dynamometer car, as are the speeds in all cases.

On the first day (Bristol-Leeds) a notable performance was over the 6.5 miles of uphill slog from Gloucester to Cheltenham, starting at 1 in 174 but mainly at 1 in 344/304/368, and run in 9min 10sec start-to-stop. Full regulator with cutoff not reduced below 35% brought speed up to 64 before shutting off. The actual DBHP varied between 1,000 and 1,140

almost throughout. The other section of note was between Burton and Clay Cross. From the 40mph slowing through Burton platform, speed was worked up to exactly 80 approaching Peartree, on nine miles of virtually level road, with actual DBHP sustained between 980 and 1,070; this probably needed 30% cutoff. From the Derby start speed reached 73 before Ambergate with actual DBHP in the 1,050-1,170 range. Then from Ambergate speed increased to 72 at Stretton, climbing all the way at about 1 in 320 average, the peak DBHP being 1,170 and the EDBHP about 1,360. No cutoff less than 35% was used on this section. The Report, a little tongue in cheek, perhaps, notes that:

'Sectional timekeeping Burton-Derby-Sheffield was maintained but the power required from the engine was very considerable.'

Thereafter, much hard but unspectacular work was done between frequent slowings on to Leeds.

Northwards from Leeds on the second day, the proved partnership of North and George contented themselves with running closely to booked times as far as practicable. Mainly 30% cutoff took the train to Settle Jc; from there up the 13.9 miles of 1 in 100 to Blea Moor 35% cutoff was sufficient for a minimum speed of 47 and a time of 16min 20sec, gaining over 1½min. The DBHP peaked at 1,240 at Helwith Bridge and remained over 1,080 throughout the climb. Running on to Carlisle was very restrained to keep within speed limits, largely to 70mph, the engine coasting from Ais Gill to beyond Ormside.

North of the Border, one can only marvel at anyone setting start-to-stop times of 18min Carlisle-Annan, 17.6 miles including a 55mph restriction over Gretna Junction, and 15½min Annan-Dumfries, 15.5 miles including the sharp rise past Ruthwell. The Report comments that 3min was lost by the engine between Carlisle and Dumfries but enigmatically says this 'was due to methods of operation', which is totally unfair to a crew being asked to do the impossible. From Dumfries to Kilmarnock time was exactly kept, with 900-1,000DBHP all the way up to Drumlanrig Tunnel, with a brief peak of 1,160DBHP and a minimum of 56mph on the 1 in 150. The climb out of Kilmarnock was taken very energetically, with actual DBHP rising to a maximum of 1,230 at Stewarton at 50mph; the minimum speed topping the 1 in 75 before Dunlop was as high as 44.

But it was on the third day that North and George, their noses pointed towards Leeds, produced the real fireworks, and Table 15 and Fig 9 show details of the performance on certain sections of this day's work.[38] Even with a cold start, the formidable Neilston bank, culminating in 3¼ miles of 1 in 67/69/70, was surmounted at a minimum of 35mph using 35% cutoff and an actual DBHP of over 1,000. From the restart from Kilmarnock speed fell to 49 on the 1 in 100, but then recovered to about 55 at Garrochburn. The Report says that 35% cutoff was used to Hurlford and 36% to Mossgiel Tunnel, but this appears inconsistent with the recorded speeds, and on the 1 in 100 the DBHP was over 1,200 for 3½ miles, implying at least 40%. The nearly four miles uphill at between 1 in 150 and 180 to Auchinleck, followed by the easier stretch past Mauchline, brought speed down to 62, and after 69 at Old Cumnock the final three miles on mainly 1 in 145/150 to Polquhap Siding produced a minimum of 63. Actual DBHP ranged from 900 to 1,080 throughout this section, with the engine working at 36%

Table 15
Dynamometer Car Test Run. 14 October 1937.
Locomotive: Class 5XP 4-6-0 No 5660 *Rooke*
Load: coaches 9
   tons tare/gross: 302/305
Enginemen: Dvr W. North, Fmn H. George (Holbeck)

Distance Miles		Test Schedule Minutes	Actual Time Min Sec	Speed
0.0	Glasgow St Enoch	0	0.00	—
	Strathbungo	4	4.10	—
7.4	Barrhead	11	10.33	63 max
10.2	mp 10¼		15.21	35 min
14.2	Lugton	21	19.12	64
18.7	Stewarton	—		71/65
24.2	Kilmarnock	31	29.47	78 max
1.8	Hurlford		3.11	56 max
9.4	Mauchline	13½	11.57	49/56/69
15.8	Old Cumnock		18.00	62/69/63
21.1	New Cumnock	27½	22.58	72/65
			pws	
31.9	Sanquhar	37½	32.25	73/25
40.5	Carronbridge	—		57/50*
43.8	Thornhill	48½	46.20	72
50.4	Auldgirth	—		67/73/62
58.0	Dumfries	62	60.11	68 max
8.5	Ruthwell		9.49	68/65
15.5	Annan	16	15.52	78 max
9.0	Gretna Jc	9	10.05	72/56*
17.6	Carlisle	19	19.49	71 max
8.4	Low House Siding		11.31	49/58/57
15.5	Lazonby	19	17.26	73/72/81/78
19.8	Langwathby		20.59	70/73/70
30.8	Appleby	35	30.20	76/67
33.3	Ormside		32.21	78 max
38.3	Crosby Garrett		37.10	59/62
44.9	Mallerstang		44.18	49/55
48.4	Ais Gill	59	48.36	45 min
59.6	Blea Moor	70	59.14	68/62
113.0	Leeds	125	115.38	—

*Permanent Speed Restriction

cutoff. The sharp timing of 16min from Dumfries to Annan was kept, but a DBHP of 1,060 maximum was needed up to Ruthwell to do it.

It was, however, on the 48-mile 'Long Drag' from Carlisle up to the 1,169ft level at Ais Gill that North and George showed what a 'Jubilee' could do when a skilled crew pushed her to the limit. The Dynamometer Car report, po-faced as usual, commented:

'Between Carlisle and Blea Moor . . . 11min were regained by the engine over the booked time, which resulted from the engine being worked harder than the special timings demanded.'

But this could hardly have been done without the connivance of the (no doubt delighted) dynamometer car crew. The record shows cutoffs of 35, 30 and 25 out to Lazonby, though this seems low in relation to the DBHP level of 1,000-1,250; likewise 35-40% is shown from Kirkby Stephen to Ais Gill, but one wonders, in view of the power level, whether the 35% did not start at Ormside, from where 1,000-1,170DBHP was the order of the day. Worthy of note are the practically sustained 47 on the 1 in 132/129 to Low House, the 70 or more held on the rising grades from Langwathby to Appleby, and the rapid accelerations at Crosby Garrett and Mallerstang where the grade eases from the ruling 1 in 100. The overall result of this effort was to better 'even time' by Appleby and to almost hold this position all the way up to the summit. The equivalent DBHP before Low House is estimated at over 1,500; the average DBHP from Ormside to Ais Gill is given in the report as 1,054, which would require an EDBHP of about 1,430.

Calculated times and speeds from Carlisle up to Ais Gill, for water rates of 20,000 and 24,000lb/hr (21,280 and 25,310lb/hr steam rates, using exhaust steam injector) based on the comparable BR Standard Class 5, make it clear that *Rooke* was being driven at about the higher rate to Howes'

Fig 9 Speed and DBHP curves, 'Jubilee' No 5660, Kilmarnock-New Cumnock and Carlisle-Ais Gill, October 1937.

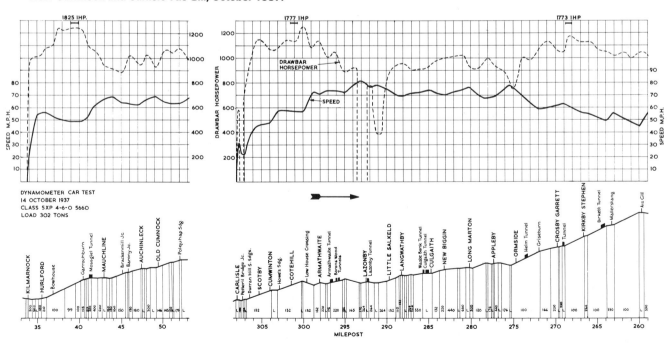

48

Siding, then was pushed still harder up to the summit at Low House, eased slightly to beyond Armathwaite, and then put at the climb to mp 295 at above the 24,000lb/hr rate. After being eased a little past Lazonby to keep within the line limit of 80mph, speeds to Culgaith match very closely the 20,000lb/hr figures, whence an intermediate rate of working applied to Ormside. On the main climb there was very close correspondence to the 24,000lb/hr speeds as far as Kirkby Stephen, but on the section to Mallerstang the working was even harder, though it fell away again on the final stage to Ais Gill, passed at 45mph minimum instead of a calculated figure of $46\frac{1}{2}$. But for over 40min *Rooke* had been steaming continuously at little under 24,000lb/hr average.

After such running, the fourth day could only be something of an anti-climax, through no fault of the enginemen. From Sheffield, 45/40/35% cutoffs were used up to Dronfield, the latter probably through the wet Bradway Tunnel, the DBHP rising to a maximum of 1,250 and the EDBHP averaging something like 1,570. From Derby, 40/35/30% cutoff worked the train to a maximum of 81mph before Burton, and after braking to 38 through the platform, 35 and 30% brought a sustained 79 on the 1 in 408/484 rise after Elford, with DBHPs between 1,030 and 1,208. The start from Gloucester on the rising gradients out to Standish Junction, including $\frac{3}{4}$-mile at 1 in 108 and $1\frac{3}{4}$ miles at 1 in 104, also using 45/40/35% cutoff, produced a speed of 57 beyond Harefield with a DBHP of 1,090-1,165.

The coal and water consumptions related to such hard work from a medium sized engine could only be fairly heavy, though masked to some extent on the Leeds-Glasgow days by lengthy periods of coasting. They were:

	12 Oct	13 Oct	14 Oct	15 Oct
Coal: lb/mile	53.7	42.7	43.6	51.1
lb/DBHP hr	4.16	3.93	3.87	3.81
lb/sq ft/hr	96.4	77.7	80.2	91.3
Water: gal/mile	33.7	29.7	28.8	35.0
lb/DBHP hr	26.1	27.3	25.5	26.2
Evaporation: lb/lb coal	6.26	6.94	6.58	6.86

On these, the Report commented:

'Although the steaming and operation of the engine was very satisfactory, the general conditions of the test, timing, speed restrictions and consequent high power development required a very high rate of combustion, and in view of this the results obtained can be considered to show fair economy.'

and concluded realistically that:

'Whilst the engine proved to be quite capable of maintaining the test schedule in all respects' (which was not *strictly* true) 'the rate of working was beyond that which could be recommended in all circumstances for daily operation'.

This was very fair; the average combustion rate on the grate must have been well over 100lb/sq ft/hr while working, requiring a high standard of firemanship, and the boiler efficiency would suffer markedly from unburnt fuel loss. The report therefore gave recommended schedules for a 5X engine with a load not exceeding 280 tons, which allowed 6min more in each direction between Bristol and Leeds than the test timings, and 2min more (Down) and 8min less (Up) between Leeds and Glasgow while omitting the Annan stop.

Lest it should be thought that *Rooke's* running was an unrepeatable special case, however, it is interesting to read an account by O. S. Nock[39] of a run in 1945 over the same route with a heavy 13-coach train.

'The point-to-point timings were exceptionally hard for wartime and Driver Walker drove the engine extremely hard on the 1 in 100 ascent . . . to Mossgiel Tunnel. At one stage . . . he was working in no less than 50% cutoff, with full regulator: but although steam pressure was well maintained, the water level was falling, and the engine had to be eased a little . . .'

But better was to come after Carlisle, left 5min late.

'Once again the driver used full regulator, and this time the cutoff was kept continuously at 44 to 42% right out to the summit point near Low House box. Here speed was absolutely sustained at $44\frac{1}{2}$mph on the 1 in 129 gradient. This time, too, both boiler pressure and water level were constant and this tremendously hard working indicated an output of 1,440EDBHP. I need hardly add that the firing was superbly well done . . . Walker used 25% cutoff in getting away from Appleby. This took us rapidly up to $52\frac{1}{2}$mph on the 1 in 182 descent to Ormside Viaduct, and the impetus thus gained enabled the first three miles of 1 in 100 ascent to be climbed without any advance in cutoff. Speed dropped to 32mph near Griseburn box, but hereabouts cutoff was advanced to 35% . . . speed rose to 49mph over Smardale Viaduct and then with cutoff advanced to 37% we sustained a very steady 38mph on the long 1 in 100 past Kirkby Stephen and into Birkett Tunnel. Steaming continued to be perfect, and water level maintained constant. The EDBHP at this point was approximately 1,400. At the south end of Birkett Tunnel suddenly we went into a heavy slip . . .'

So much for five years of wartime neglect!

Brief mention may be made of a series of dynamometer car tests in May 1938 of No 5606 fitted with TAB piston valves, a proprietary design whose valve heads were free to move on the valve spindles. In normal working, steam chest pressure held the heads in the usual position on to stop collars on the spindle, but when coasting they were released to take up positions closer together, effecting a complete bye-pass. The tests were run between Crewe and Carlisle, for one week with the TAB valves and one week with standard valves, and Dynamometer Car Report No 76 shows that there was no significant effect on coal consumption. The TAB valves made the engine extremely free running when coasting (done in mid gear), but there was some leakage and occasional malfunction of the TAB valves giving incomplete bye-pass, and the decision was taken not to proceed further.

Still in pursuit of any aid which would exploit the optimum in performance, another special fitting, the Loco Valve Pilot, was tested in January 1939, fitted to 'Jubilee' No 5654. This device, manufactured and widely used in the USA, was essentially a speedometer fitted with a second pointer linked to the reversing gear via a cam, profiled to suit the characteristics of the locomotive. If the engine were driven in such a way as to keep the 'cutoff' pointer coincident with the speed pointer, the engine would (at least in theory) be working within its economic power range.

The engine was tested between Derby and St Pancras. It transpired on the first day of driving to the Valve Pilot that the engine was not keeping time; the cam was therefore modified rather hastily overnight to give what Dynamometer Car Report No 79 laconically called 'an approximate correction', and for the next three days attempts were made to drive as indicated. But with trains varying from 259 to 318 tons:

'... the cutoff hand of the Valve Pilot indicator had to be 10-20mph in front of the speed indicator hand in order to maintain sectional running times, otherwise time would have been gained unnecessarily.'

Perhaps the hand that wielded the file overnight had been too heavy! There were, however, justifiable doubts about the correct cam profile, keeping the mechanism in accurate adjustment, and how to guide drivers in its proper use in a variety of day-to-day circumstances, which led to the device being dropped.

Just before World War 2 put a stop to any further innovation a final modification was made to two 'Jubilees' associated with their steaming qualities. This was probably triggered off by the *Duchess of Abercorn* maximum load tests in February 1939, which showed a big improvement in boiler output after fitting a plain double blastpipe and chimney. Nos 5553 and 5742 were fitted in 1940 with similar double blastpipes and chimneys, the order calling for fitment to one straight and one sloping throatplate boiler; the blastpipe caps were 3⅝in dia (equivalent in area to a single 5⅛in cap) and exhausting through chimney chokes 1ft 1⅛in dia. Little is known about the fitting on No 5553, which apparently did not last long, but No 5742 carried her double chimney until renewal was needed in 1955, when she reverted to standard. From the author's experience on the footplate (see Chapter 6) the steaming of this engine was impeccable, though with some tendency to throw more fire than with the standard draughting, but no official tests seem to have been run.

Though not strictly within the time-span of this chapter, it seems appropriate to mention here a last series of 'Jubilee' tests made under the auspices of the LMS after the war, in February/March 1946. Some disappointment evidently still lurked at Derby that, even with the line 15 boiler with 24-element superheater, steam temperatures seldom rose above 640°F even when working very hard; at the same time the front end condition suggested that the lubrication of cylinders and valves would not be distressed by some increase. This was the background to the fitting of No 5733 with a set of the French 'Houlet' superheater elements[40] for comparison with bifurcated and wartime return loop elements. Actually, for some reason only 21 'Houlet' elements were available, and so three bifurcated elements were used to make up the 'set'! Trials were run between Crewe and Shrewsbury with 450 ton loads, recording stream chest pressure and steam and exhaust temperatures on selected sections of line where the engine needed to be worked hard.

The results were reported in a CME memorandum of 10 April thus:

'A sustained steam chest temperature of 680-700°F and a maximum temperature of 742°F was obtained with the 'Houlet' elements compared with a sustained temperature of 620-630°F and a maximum temperature of 670°F for the standard types of elements... With (the latter) there was no definite indication of any superheat in the exhaust. With the 'Houlet' elements... there appears to be ... 30-50°F superheat in the exhaust steam...'

The 'Houlet' elements appeared to adversely affect the steaming slightly, particularly under heavy working conditions. No further action was taken to use these elements on other engines.

Right: In full cry as she leaves Edge Hill station behind, 'Jubilee' No 5587 *Baroda* on the Up 'Sunny South Express' (1937).
Eric Treacy/P. B. Whitehouse collection

Above left: No 5621 *Northern Rhodesia*, in 1936 style livery following fitting with sloping throatplate boiler, is at grips with the 1 in 75 gradient past Horfield working the Up 'Devonian'.   *Real Photos 3866*

Left: An interesting job for a 'Jubilee' in 1937 — no less than the 14-coach 20.30 Down 'West Coast Postal'. The driver of No 5659 *Drake* keeps his head in as the pouches hang on the Harrow lineside apparatus, awaiting the extended net on the eighth vehicle.
Real Photos 24188

Below: 'Jubilee' No 5734 *Meteor* is heading an express at an unidentified West Coast main line location, and leaving a clean trail of steam in the crisp winter air.
Ian Allan Library

Above right: No 5558 *Manitoba* passes Bourne End with a light Up milk train for Kensington in 1938.
Real Photos 24112

Right: 'Jubilee' No 5606, unnamed, approaches Mangotsfield on a stopping train early in 1938. The engine is carrying indicator shelters in connection with the tests of TAB experimental piston valves. After abortive trials with the original boiler, she was fitted with a sloping throatplate boiler before the tests in May referred to in this chapter. *Real Photos 3864*

Below: No 5669 *Fisher* coasts on to Dillicar troughs with a Down express freight before stopping at Tebay for an assisting engine in rear up to Shap Summit. (1938).
M. W. Earley

Top: No 5603 blasts her way up the 1 in 93 to Edge Hill on an Up Euston express in 1939. The fireman looks relaxed, and has apparently not noticed that his exhaust steam injector has 'knocked off'.
Eric Treacy/P. B. Whitehouse collection

Above: 'Jubilee' No 5691 *Orion* will be doing a mile-a-minute as she passes mp 17, just south of Watford Junction, on a 12-coach Down express in 1939 — and showing a white feather at the safety valves. *Real Photos 24120*

Right: Class 5 No 5275 is seen at Wickwar on a Down express in 1937.
Real Photos 879

Below right: No 5389 makes easy work of a five-coach plus horsebox Down semi-fast at Yate in 1938.
Real Photos 2522

Bottom right: Class 5 No 5432, which came to the Somerset & Dorset Joint line in 1938, is here seen hustling a light Down stopping passenger train past Midford. Note the unique 'passenger' lamp headcode used on this line. *Real Photos 1804*

Far right, top: Assisted in rear, No 5106 from Kingmoor shed blasts past Scout Green box, on the 1 in 75 of Shap bank, on a Down through freight in 1939.
Eric Treacy/P. B. Whitehouse collection

Far right, bottom: A Midland Division regular, No 5262 emerges from Ambergate Tunnel with the southbound 'Devonian'. *Real Photos 2534*

Top: No 5301 has her work cut out as she lifts a 12-coach express for Carlisle out of Preston in 1939.
Eric Treacy/P. B. Whitehouse collection

Above: On the mainly level grades of the North Wales coast line, No 5346 will not be unduly taxed on a six-coach stopping train.
Eric Treacy/P. B. Whitehouse collection

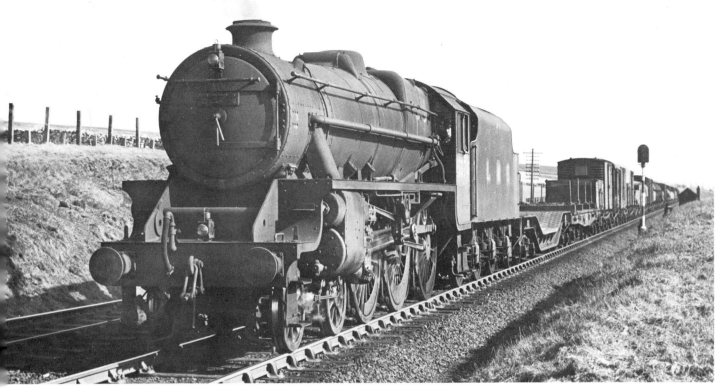

Above: A grubby No 5374 is working hard on a Down through freight, assisted in rear, as she passes the Shap Wells intermediate block distant signal.
Eric Treacy/P. B. Whitehouse collection

Left: In 1939 'Jubilee' No 5698 *Mars* was fitted with a smokebox ash ejector device for use on depots. The cleaning jets took hot water from the live steam injector delivery pipe, and were controlled from the valve manifold behind the main steam pipe. *Real Photos 2797*

Below left: A somewhat similar experimental device was fitted to No 5671 *Prince Rupert* in 1942, the jets being controlled from a rotary distributor on the smokebox side. Both these devices were superseded by the self-cleaning smokebox, which avoided the corrosion problem of water in the smokebox bottom, though not on the 'Jubilees'.
Real Photos W7719

5

Design Developments

Standardisation is an aim to be pursued in the interests of efficiency, and the locomotive field is no exception to this truism. But with items having a built-in life expectancy of 30-50 years, the rigid application of standardisation over a long period can lead to stagnation and the sudden realisation that one's assets, excellent by the criteria of twenty years before, are no longer leaders in their field (as one railway in Britain discovered in the 1940s). The LMS, while perhaps not quite so innovative as the prewar LNER, took a lead when hostilities ended, in the development of variations of its basic designs, with (generally) greater mechanical endurance and reliability, ease of servicing and extended shopping periods in mind, though a very small amount of re-building to give increased power ratings was also undertaken.

The LMS was never flush for large power; the operating case for more big engines just did not get adequately made. In 1940 the LMS front-line passenger engine fleet comprised little over 100 engines, namely:

Class 7P 4-6-2 'Princess'	12 (plus 'Turbomotive')
Class 7P 4-6-2 'Duchess'	25
Class 6P 4-6-0 'Royal Scot'	71

Some 37 Pacifics were a small enough group in all conscience to work the hardest turns, with only the 71 large 4-6-0s or some double-headed combination to support and substitute for them. Behind these came the fairly plentiful group of 52 'Patriots' and 191 'Jubilees', competent within their 5XP classification but by no stretch of the imagination large engines. Both in the immediate prewar years, and during the war, they had to undertake duties which pushed them right up to, if not beyond, the limit of what could be reliably expected in day-to-day operation.

But since 1935 one large 4-6-0 had been showing itself to stand out above the parallel-boilered 'Royal Scots' — the rebuild, No 6170 *British Legion*. The No 2 tapered boiler used on No 6170 was good, even if not ideal. The sloping throatplate firebox could not be faulted, but the barrel was rather long in relation to the chassis, being 14ft 3in between tubeplates, putting too much weight to the front end. The 28-element superheater was suitable, but the $1\frac{7}{8}$in dia small tubes, with an A/S ratio of 1/422, were a little constricted. The total free gas area was ample, at 5.17sq ft (16.5% of grate area), the superheater contributing 48.7% of the total. A single blastpipe with $4\frac{7}{8}$in dia cap was fitted, as on the parallel boiler engines.

Dynamometer car trials with No 6170 between Liverpool and Euston in April 1939 has shown that the engine in this form did its work with reasonable efficiency and that the steaming was 'consistent in character and adequate' — hardly a paeon of praise. By now, the crucial ratios for a successful boiler were well understood, so that here was a guide to what might be achieved by rebuilding 5X's, with benefit to their haulage capabilities.

Earlier, in 1937, the Development Drawing Office at Derby had produced an outline scheme for a two-cylinder version of the 'Jubilee' using the boiler design of No 6170 (see Chapter 7). This proposal was shelved, only to be revived in 1938/9. Eric Langridge has related[42] how:

'Coleman (Chief Draughtsman) had the idea of putting the "Scot" boiler on the 5X chassis ... he came out one day with the order to see if it could be done and what sort of weights we should get ... the best we could do without alteration to frames was practically nil. So we took the bull by the horns, and suggested lopping a bit off the taper "Scot" barrel and making a new cylinder pattern to suit. When Coleman said "Cut up the taper 'Scot' inside cylinder pattern" I said to him "What if No 6170 wants a new cylinder?". He just said "Don't worry about that". I thought he had gone out of his mind! However, that is what we did: it was a bit rough on the 5X frame to load it up with a large boiler, but as only two were to be tried out I thought we might improve things if the rebuilding was successful.'

The design of the revised boiler was put in hand in 1939 at Derby. The *British Legion* firebox dimensions were unchanged, but a new boiler barrel was grafted on, 15in shorter but $\frac{1}{2}$in larger in diameter on the front ring, giving a length between tubeplates of 13ft 0in. With shorter tubes a new tubeplate layout providing 28 superheater elements and 198 small tubes $1\frac{1}{4}$in dia was worked out, giving a total free gas area of 5.09sq ft (16.3% of grate area), the superheater contributing 49.5% of this. The small tubes now had an A/S ratio of 1/411, which could hardly be bettered. The reboilering increased the overall weight by no more than 2.45 tons, with a maximum axleload of 20.75 tons, which was acceptable for route availability purposes. The rebuild involved only limited alteration to the chassis. The new boiler was complemented by a plain double blastpipe and chimney in the general style of those fitted to Nos 5553 and 5742 in 1940, the blastpipe caps being $3\frac{3}{4}$in dia (standard with those used later on the 'Royal Scot' rebuilds). Authority was given in 1940 for the conversion of two engines, but under wartime conditions it was April 1942 before the first engine, No 5736, came from Crewe works, followed the next month by No 5735.

The two engines made their wartime debut based at Leeds Holbeck, where they immediately established new levels of performance working over the Settle & Carlisle and G&SW route to Glasgow. An extract from a published run[42] in 1943

Table 16

13.55 Carlisle-Glasgow St Enoch
Locomotive: Class 5XP 4-6-0 No 5736 *Phoenix**
Load: coaches 12
      tons tare/gross 379/430
Enginemen: Dvr A. Davis (Corkerhill)

Distance Miles		Schedule Min	Actual Time Min	Sec	Speed
0.0	Dumfries	0	0.00		—
				pws	28
7.6	Auldgirth		12.03		—
11.4	Closeburn		17.08		48/56
14.2	Thornhill	19	20.14		54
17.5	Carronbridge		24.06		50 min
21.2	Ardoch		27.56		70
26.1	Sanquhar	33	32.40		58
29.4	Kirkconnel		35.58		66/59
36.9	New Cumnock	45	43.17		70
42.2	Old Cumnock		48.14		—
				signals	
48.6	Mauchline	58	56.21		—
56.2	Hurlford		63.41		72 max
58.0	Kilmarnock	70	66.21		—

Net Time: 61min
*Subsequently reclassed 6P

is set out in Table 16. On the long 1 in 150 climb from Closeburn to Drumlanrig Tunnel, made at a minimum of 48mph, No 5736's calculated EDBHP was of the order of 1,420, and it is interesting to note that the time of 46min 7sec from passing Thornhill to the Kilmarnock stop actually bettered that of the *Rooke* trial by 23sec, notwithstanding the signal check at Brackenhill Junction — and this in 1943!

In May 1945 rebuilt 'Jubilee' No 5736 was tested between Crewe and Carlisle with the dynamometer car in comparison with rebuilt 'Scot' No 6131 (having the same type '2A' boiler) and parallel boilered engine No 6162:

'... to ascertain the coal and water consumptions of two types of engine fitted with the same type of boiler ...'

The trains ran on unexciting 'Full Load' timings for which Class 6 engines were allowed 465 tons from Carnforth and Carlisle to Shap Summit; Nos 5736 and 6131 actually took 449 tons, while No 6162 was slightly more heavily loaded. Dynamometer Car Report No 82 shows that, despite the presence of a Motive Power Inspector in the cab, there tended to be considerable variation in engine handling, due to multiple crewing, with No 5736 generally being worked on longer cutoffs (16-25% on level and easier grades, as compared with 12-20% for No 6131, while northbound to Shap Summit she was worked at up to 50% against 38% with No 6131. The steaming of No 5736 was as near perfect as could be desired, whereas 6131 flagged a little on the final stages to Shap Summit. The consumption figures were:

Engine	5736	6131	6162
Coal: lb/mile	47.1	53.2	54.8
lb/DBHP hr	4.00	4.02	4.26
lb/sq ft/hr	67.3	75.0	80.5
Water: gal/mile	35.3	39.1	38.4
lb/DBHP hr	30.1	29.6	29.8
Evaporation: lb/lb coal	7.53	7.35	7.00

The conclusions of the report were not profound, drawing attention to the lower specific coal consumptions of the taper

boilered engines and the ability of the 'Royal Scot' with 18in cylinders to run at shorter cutoffs than the 'Jubilee' rebuild with 17in cylinders.

Despite the increased haulage potential given by the '2A' boiler, no further 'Jubilees' were converted, probably due to the inherent long life of the relatively new '3A' boilers on them. Instead, priority was given to a more extensive rebuilding of the 'Patriots', in similar form, starting in 1946; by this time some of the G9½S boilers were 18 years old. Only 18 'Patriots' were so modified before work ceased in 1949, the LM Region incredibly taking the view that traffic requirements did not warrant any more conversions. Meanwhile the two 'Jubilee' rebuilds gravitated to the Western Division, taking their places alongside the other Class 6P (later 7P) rebuilds. They seemed to have no unusual weaknesses, save for some early rough riding and frame fractures. The coupled axleboxes were fitted with manganese steel liners in the early 1950s, and the standard 'Royal Scot' type smoke deflectors were added at about the same time.

There was, however, one recorded instance of one of these engines putting up a remarkable performance in circumstances of some difficulty. One afternoon in 1958, the 'Duchess' working the Up 'Caledonian' from Glasgow Central became a casualty and had to be taken off at Carlisle. The only available replacement was No 45736 *Phoenix*.[43] The 'Caledonian' was a fairly light formation of only eight coaches, 266 tons, and after Carlisle made a single stop, at Stafford. Over the Carlisle-Stafford section, including the climb to Shap, it was allowed 172 minutes for the 165.5 miles, representing fractionally under 58mph, but after that it became the fastest train on the LM Region, being required to average 66.8mph over the 133.6 miles to Euston. Moreover, the train was 22min late away from Carlisle, and it is doubtful whether *Phoenix* had been prepared by the Upperby crew who worked it to Euston, thus perhaps lacking the finer touches which can lead to a good start on an initially difficult road. But the crew were determined to do every bit as well as if they had had a Pacific. By Crewe they had picked up 11min of the late start, and were only 9min late from Stafford. Table 17 now takes up the story.

I would estimate that the second valve of the regulator was in extensive use, although *Phoenix* was being driven on a comparatively light rein. The uphill power outputs were not unduly high, as befitted the modest load — 1,070EDBHP at Bulkington in accelerating to 68 on 1 in 320, no greater fall than from 79½ to 75 over the Roade hump, and 1,100EDBHP in breasting the 1 in 333 to Tring at a minimum of 72. The level and easy stretches were run at a steady 80 and more, and the 118.9 miles from Rugeley to Willesden were run at an average of 74.5mph, despite the permanent way slack between Polesworth and Atherstone, and the Rugby slack. The 67.2 miles from Welton to Wembley were reeled off at an average of 78.9mph, with nothing higher than 87. A finely judged, even performance which, coming in the later stages of a 300-mile run, did great credit to the crew. They deserved better than to then spend a noisy night in the Camden hostel!

C. E. Fairburn became CME at the beginning of 1943, and during his brief period of office, in response to the harsh conditions of maintenance which had developed during World War 2, a period of continuous development of steam locomotive design began to make them fit for a hard world; to make them rugged, to minimise servicing and maintenance work at running sheds, and to extend shopping mileages. This

Table 17

The 'Caledonian', 16.00 Glasgow Cen-Euston
Locomotive: Class 7P 4-6-0 No 45736 *Phoenix*
Load: coaches 8
        tons tare/gross 266/280
Enginemen: Dvr Stalker, Fmn Pinner (Upperby)

Distance Miles		Schedule Minutes	Actual Time Min Sec		Speed
0.0	Stafford	0	0.00		—
4.1	Milford & Brockton	5	6.00		67
9.3	Rugeley	10	10.17		78/80
12.6	Armitage		12.48		76
17.3	Lichfield	16	16.33		80/85½
23.6	Tamworth	22	21.00		82
27.1	Polesworth		23.40		77½
			pws		35
36.5	Nuneaton	34	33.07		67
40.1	Bulkington		36.21		68
45.5	Brinklow		40.45		80
51.0	Rugby	48	45.10		49*
58.3	Welton		52.50		64/68½
63.9	Weedon	59	57.11		82½
70.8	Blisworth	64	62.21		79½/75
73.7	Roade	67	64.40		77
81.2	Wolverton		70.02		87/82
86.9	Bletchley	78	74.21		80
93.4	Leighton Buzzard		79.14		78/81
97.5	Cheddington		82.24		75
101.9	Tring	91	86.02		72
109.1	Hemel Hempstead		91.29		85/83
116.2	Watford Jc	102	96.32		86¼/80
122.2	Harrow		101.25		73/78
128.2	Willesden Jc	112	106.03		81/65*
133.6	Euston	120	113.34		—

Net Time: 111½min
*Permanent Speed Restriction

process was intensified under H. G. Ivatt, and really took two roads in parallel; firstly in attention to, and refinement of, detail[44], and secondly in testing more fundamental developments such as roller bearings and poppet valve gears. The Class 5s, in continuing new production, were the principal vehicles for introducing all these new features.

The first issue tackled was that of axlebox wear and knock. In 1951, Class 5s with whitemetal-faced axleboxes were averaging 56,969 miles system-wide between periodical repairs[45] and the 'Jubilees' rather more; this shopping was, of course, dictated also by tyre wear and boiler examination findings, but axlebox condition was an important factor. With Class 5s of the Nos 4807-4825 batch a trial was made of bronze liners on the coupled axleboxes, as was common on the GWR and SR, the face liners being secured to the steel carcase by copper studs riveted down, and the flange liners riveted through. It was found that wear was somewhat better than with whitemetal, but difficulties arose due to loosening, and even complete loss, of liners when the fastenings broke down under the heavy pounding experienced in service. In due course, therefore, they were replaced.

About 1946 a start was made with fitting new Class 5s with manganese steel liners on the coupled axlebox faces and flanges, and on the axlebox guides and hornblocks. After some changes in the securing of the liners to the axlebox carcase, these proved eminently successful (Fig 10). Some of the first engines fitted went to Perth, where they ran up to 200,000 miles, and in at least one case more, before shopping; even then it was for tyre wear or boiler attention rather than axlebox wear. At the same time, the hornstay weakness was tackled along the lines suggested by the Research investi-

gation of 1943/4. The Horwich type hornstay, bolted direct to the frame plate, was adopted for all new construction in 1945, with the improvement that the mating faces were deepened to 6in to give greater bearing area.[45] This design proved every bit as successful on Class 5s and (retrospectively) 'Jubilees' — and on other classes to which it was applied — as on the original 2-6-0s.

The spring gear, too, came in for attention, influenced by experience during World War 2 with US-built 2-8-0s. About 1947 a changeover was made on new Class 5s from screwed tension coupled spring links to flat section links, with massive box-section spring link brackets, the weight being transferred through interchangeable flat cotters inserted in each end of the link; these cotters were made in a range of depths to provide weight adjustment.[46] A small hydraulic jack placed on top of the spring near the link allowed the spring end to be jacked down to release the cotters for exchange. Shortly after, the practice was standardised in the works of setting up the back end of the engine with about 1⅞in clearance over the coupled axleboxes (⅜in more than drawing), so that the initial loss of spring camber would bring the engine down to its design height (See Appendix 5).

The effect of these modifications on the Class 5s — admittedly on relatively new engines — was to increase the mileage of the manganese steel linered engines in 1951 to an average of 97,291 miles between periodical repairs.[45] As a result, in 1951 authority was given for all Class 5s to be fitted retrospectively with manganese steel liners, and for the 'Jubilees' to be brought into line also. The case for doing this was largely based on the economics of eliminating one of the usual two Intermediate Repairs between General Repairs. Existing Class 5s receiving this modification were also fitted with cottered spring links, but this alteration was not

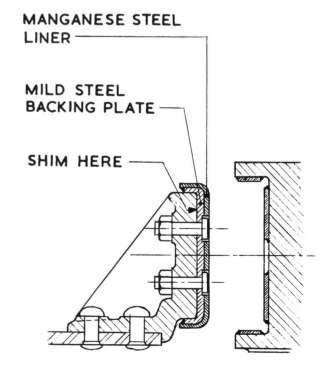

Fig 10 Manganese steel axlebox liners.

MANGANESE STEEL LINER

MILD STEEL BACKING PLATE

SHIM HERE

extended to the 'Jubilees'. Unfortunately, perhaps the work was never completed due to the dieselisation programme.

The brake rigging was altered, too, to provide twin brake blocks on each hanger, giving a much longer life between reblockings.

The simple box piston head screwed directly on to the rod, with its inherent liability to flaw, was changed postwar; while the head itself was little changed, it was now nutted up to a collar on the rod. This method of fastening required a little development to get it right, but was soon finalised as right and left hand threaded nuts with heavy tab washer between them.

Next to be modified were the piston valves, whose rings could so easily be broken when inserting the back head through the front liner. The guide ribs machined in the steam chest[9] seldom gave smooth entry into the bellmouth of the back liner. Indeed, at Rowsley the author watched with dismay, after seeing the valves replaced with loving care in a Class 4 2-6-0, when as the engine was moved for lighting-up the combination lever slowly bent into a 30° arc due to a broken ring trapped in the port. The solution proved to be what became known as 'differential' valve heads, the back liners and heads being machined $\frac{1}{8}$in smaller on diameter than nominal for easy insertion, and this was adopted universally. The unbalanced force on the valve when under steam produced no ill-effects on the valve gear.

Now the smokebox came in for attention. The aims were three-fold — to keep the smokebox clear of char, to keep the tubes clear, and to prevent the emission of sparks big enough to cause lineside fires — while not adversely affecting steaming. The engines had originally been fitted with deflector plates based on the American 'Master Mechanics' front end; wire mesh screens to break up cinders were now added in front of the blastpipe and chimney, and the table plate turned down at the front edge to give a keen scouring effect at the base of the smokebox. This was the 'self-cleaning' smokebox used on later Class 5s and several other classes, and which proved so successful after minor 'tuning'. It proved a godsend to hard-pressed depots, for now smokebox doors bearing the 'SC' plate were only opened every 12-16 days at washouts, and smokebox and tubes remained remarkably clean. But retrospective fitting to earlier Class 5s and 'Jubilees' was not considered justified.

At the other end of the boiler, the grate and ashpan were tackled to get rid of arduous and filthy work on the ashpits. After some prototype trials on a few Class 8F 2-8-0s, Ivatt started to fit rocking grates and hopper ashpans to new Class 5s. The concept was that when running the grate was shaken, say, every half hour; by doing this much of the ash which might fuse into large sheets of clinker would be agitated into the ashpan, thus making the cleaning of the fire easier at disposal. Two degrees of rock were provided, a modest 'shake' movement to get rid of loose ash while running, and a full 'dump' movement for disposal of clinker, etc, into the ashpan. To break up such clinker, the edges of the rocking sections were soon serrated to provide teeth. The operating stubs below the firehole doors, and the detachable operating handle, underwent changes over the years to provide a more secure hold, because if the handle came off — as it did occasionally — when the fireman was vigorously operating the gear the results could be very unpleasant. In practice it was not common to see the grate shaken en route. There was both laziness and some fear of broken grate sections (which would cause a total failure) and unless

enginemen were short of steam and the fire choked, they would leave it alone to await the ministrations of the ashpit men. Rocking grates and hopper ashpans were never applied retrospectively.

Attention was now given to the problem of top feed leakage, and in 1947 Class 5s started to appear with the topfeed moved forward to the front ring of the boiler barrel. The outer casing hid a new design of manhole cover, derived from that used on the 'Duchesses', in which the clack valve cages were inserted directly into housings in the cover; separate clackboxes were abolished.

While all these changes were being designed and progressively implemented in new construction, the big developments were being planned for introduction into particular batches of 10 or 20 Class 5s for evaluation in traffic. A costing scheme was restarted, on a much smaller scale than prewar, in which all maintenance costs for these engine variations were recorded for comparison with the standard Walschaerts/Manganese liner engines, together with details of availability and mileage. Coal loaded to engines was not, however, included because coaling plants had lost the means to record it. (See Appendix 6).

The first major change was an all-axle application of roller bearing axleboxes; they were expected to complete the process of eliminating axlebox wear, with its effect on shopping. To this end, a group of 20 engines, Nos 4748-4767, was built with oil-lubricated Timken roller bearings in cannon-type axleboxes on all axles at Crewe during late 1947 and 1948. These axleboxes needed wider horngaps, which in turn, necessitated an increase in wheelbase between driving and trailing axles from 8ft 0in to 8ft 4in. Pressure from rivals SKF led to their bearings being included in the comparison. About this time, some doubts arose about the wisdom of fitting roller bearings to *all* coupled axles, following cases of high speed slipping in service resulting in bent coupling rods and shifted wheels; it was felt that this might result in a machine that was very 'tight'. This led to 20 engines being built during 1950 with SKF bearings, Nos 4668-4677 with only the driving axle so fitted, and Nos 4678-4687 with all axles fitted. These bearings were grease-lubricated and the axleboxes were separate. Finally, to complete the comparision, 10 engines, Nos 4688-4697, also appeared in 1949 with Timken cannon boxes on the driving axle only.

I had some experience of the Timken all-axle engines, and they certainly rode very sweetly and quietly, without knock — in fact, it was possible to hear railjoints clearly and clock speeds that way, and that was somewhat unusual on a two-cylinder engine.

Superimposed on the roller bearing trials were three valve gear changes, the first involving Stephenson valve gear with normal piston valves, and the other two the use of British-Caprotti poppet valve gear manufactured by Associated Locomotive Equipment Co of Worcester.

The use of Stephenson valve gear, mounted outside for full accessibility, arose as something of a joke after Ivatt had dropped a quiet hint (or challenge) to Coleman, the Chief Draughtsman, early in 1947 to beat the GWR at their own game; arguments might rage about the relative merits of fixed lead (Walschaerts) and variable lead (Stephenson), but Ivatt would never have put Stephenson gear between the frames on a Class 5. An outline design for a long-lap Stephenson gear was worked up, driven from a double outside return crank, and this so took Ivatt's fancy that No 4767 appeared with this arrangement in December 1947. The lap ($1\frac{1}{2}$in) and exhaust clearance ($\frac{1}{16}$in) remained the same as on the Walschaerts engines, but the lead increased to a maximum of $\frac{3}{8}$in in mid-gear.

No 4767 always had the reputation of being a 'strong' engine, but she never ran as sweetly as a Walschaerts engine with chassis and valves accurately set up, and there tended to be a hint of axlebox knock at all times.

In February 1948 the first of 20 Class 5s with British-Caprotti valve gear appeared from Crewe, the remainder emerging over the next 10 months. The first 10, Nos 4748-4657, had Timken bearings on all axles, while the next 10, Nos 4738-4747, had plain bearings for comparision. This valve gear had previously been applied on a very limited scale in Britain, and there was some dabbling with applications abroad, notably in Italy and India; in most cases it was a substitute for an indifferent conventional gear with piston valves. In the case of the ex-LNWR 'Claughtons', prewar dynamometer car trials had shown no very significant gain in efficiency over the Walschaerts engines,[47] even though the latter had a relatively short-lap, short-travel gear. In the Class 5 application the Caprotti valve gear, despite all its theoretical advantages, was not expected to show any marked improvement in performance or efficiency, but was fitted primarily to push up the valve and piston mileage between examinations from 30-36,000 to 40-48,000 miles, and to reduce the work content of that examination. For some years the examination mileage was not increased, until experience had been gained.

The gear was driven by a shaft between the frames, and the valves were lifted on to their seats by steam pressure when the regulator was open, the actuation steam coming from an extra port in the regulator head. When the regulator was closed the valves dropped, giving a full bye-pass for coasting. Drivers were instructed that the regulator must always be *fully* closed when coasting — very few did otherwise anyway — or actuation steam at low pressure could allow the valves to chatter, causing damage. Secondly, when reversing it was necessary to wind the reversing gear all the way to the *full* opposite gear, otherwise the pawls would not engage the camshaft driving dogs and the gear would not reverse.

The first engines brought quick complaints that they were very weak on banks; a particular instance was in starting from Bristol on the severe climb from Lawrence Hill Junction to Fishponds, mainly at 1 in 69/81/88/67, which always needed a vigorous attack. The Caprotti's made terribly heavy weather of it, though on easier roads they would run fast and coast very freely. Discussions with the manufacturers suggested that the exhaust events were to blame, notably the early compression (see Appendix 3). A modification involving auxiliary exhaust cams was then made to the camboxes, and No 44755 was indicated between Crewe and Liverpool in August 1948, with and without the auxiliary cams. The records which survive quote limited examples of mean effective pressures for cutoffs from 3% to 30%, but are inconclusive and more notable for a redistribution of work from back to front of the cylinders. In comparison with indicator cards taken on No 5051 in 1945, even the Caprotti engine with auxiliary exhaust cams was on balance weaker. The principal revelation, however, was that the cutoff plate in the cab was wildly wrong; at 20% on the plate the actual cutoff (from indicator cards) was about 13%, at 40% was actually about 26%, at 60% was in reality about 40%, and in full gear was little over 70%. All the cutoff indicator plates were

hurriedly changed to give drivers relatiively accurate information, although this caused some suspicion.

Following further discussion with the makers on the exhaust cam design, a new arrangement was schemed out using a single 'solid' cam, retaining the catches and pawls for reversing, and these new exhaust cams were fitted as camboxes went through Crewe works. The general concensus of opinion amongst enginemen was that the engines so modified were improved, but that at speeds up to about 40mph they were not the equal of a piston valve engine; however, when driven with the regulator wide open and on an appropriate cutoff, the inferiority was not great.

There were some other teething troubles. The original needle roller bearings in the drive shaft universal joints were replaced by plain bushes. There were cases of valves sticking open, causing a heavy blow up the chimney; when inlet valves were involved this was usually a result of priming, and on the exhaust side by fine particles of char. Often the valves could be freed without stripping, by soaking the valve spindle guides with penetrating oil. There were odd cases of valve and seating damage, thought to be due to valve chatter. But once the gear had settled down, the examination mileage was extended to 40-48,000 miles, at which only valve cleaning and regrinding, and gauging of clearances after assembly, were needed. The front end generally kept much cleaner than on a piston valve engine due to the bye-pass feature when coasting.

A series of indicator tests was made from October 1948 to February 1949 on these valve gear variants, mainly on service trains, using:

No 44767 with Stephenson valve gear,
No 44766 with Walschaerts valve gear and varied settings, and
No 44752 with Caprotti valve gear (at Rugby Testing Station).

Fortunately, indicator card charts for Nos 44767 and 44766 have survived, but none for No 44752 now can be traced, although some numerate information remains. There is considerable difficulty in comparing the power outputs derived from the cards, due to various inconsistencies, but they appear to suggest that as compared with the standard Walschaerts engine with nominal $\frac{1}{4}$in lead:

— a reduction in lead to $\frac{3}{16}$in resulted in a very marked loss of power particularly at the higher speeds,
— the Stephenson gear produced IHP's lower than the Walschaerts engine with $\frac{1}{4}$in lead but better than with $\frac{3}{16}$in lead, and
— the Caprotti gear gave marginally lower outputs at longer cutoffs, but higher powers on cutoffs shorter than 25% at speeds over 45mph.

Not all of this is consistent with the evidence of the footplate. Fig 11 reproduces cards from the piston valve engines, from which it will be seen that difficulty arose in balancing the work at each end of the cylinders, and quite minor changes in valve setting affected this substantially. In this connection see Appendix 6.

To complete the Caprotti story, the LM Region experience with the first 20 engines led to a redesign by ALE to meet railway requirements. Apart from the outside drive, giving better accessibility and easier applicatiion to roller bearing

Fig 11 Indicator diagrams, Class 5 Nos 44766 and 44767.

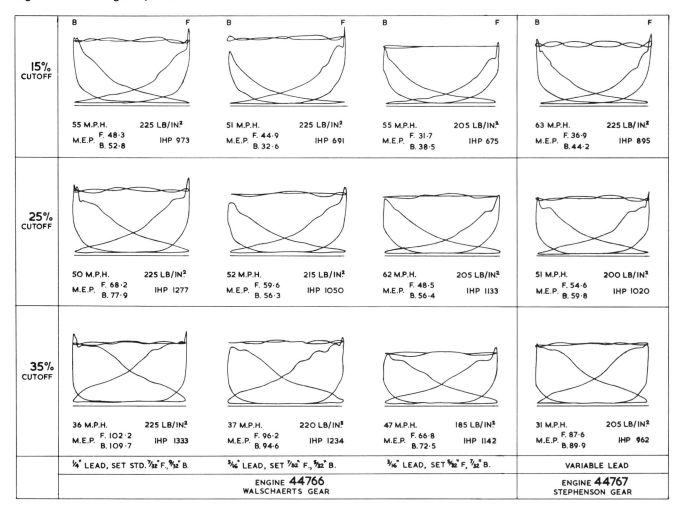

	B F	B F	B F	B F
15% CUTOFF	55 M.P.H. 225 LB/IN² M.E.P. F. 48·3 B. 52·8 IHP 973	51 M.P.H. 225 LB/IN² M.E.P. F. 44·9 B. 32·6 IHP 691	55 M.P.H. 205 LB/IN² M.E.P. F. 31·7 B. 38·5 IHP 675	63 M.P.H. 225 LB/IN² M.E.P. F. 36·9 B. 44·2 IHP 895
25% CUTOFF	50 M.P.H. 225 LB/IN² M.E.P. F. 68·2 B. 77·9 IHP 1277	52 M.P.H. 215 LB/IN² M.E.P. F. 59·6 B. 56·3 IHP 1050	62 M.P.H. 205 LB/IN² M.E.P. F. 48·5 B. 56·4 IHP 1133	51 M.P.H. 200 LB/IN² M.E.P. F. 54·6 B. 59·8 IHP 1020
35% CUTOFF	36 M.P.H. 225 LB/IN² M.E.P. F. 102·2 B. 109·7 IHP 1333	37 M.P.H. 220 LB/IN² M.E.P. F. 96·2 B. 94·6 IHP 1234	47 M.P.H. 185 LB/IN² M.E.P. F. 66·8 B. 72·5 IHP 1142	31 M.P.H. 205 LB/IN² M.E.P. F. 87·6 B. 89·9 IHP 962
	¼" LEAD, SET STD. ⁷⁄₃₂" F., ⁹⁄₃₂" B.	³⁄₁₆" LEAD, SET ⁷⁄₃₂" F., ⁵⁄₃₂" B.	³⁄₁₆" LEAD, SET ⁵⁄₃₂" F., ⁷⁄₃₂" B.	VARIABLE LEAD
	ENGINE **44766** WALSCHAERTS GEAR			ENGINE **44767** STEPHENSON GEAR

engines, the camboxes were re-thought to give better enclosure, and had twin exhaust cams to give greater variation of compression as cutoff changed. The driving dogs and pawls were eliminated, and with them the need to go into full opposite gear to reverse, so that with this form of Caprotti gear engines could be driven exactly like a piston valve engine.

Two engines, Nos 44686/7 — the last LM Class 5s to be built — emerged from Horwich with this gear in April and May 1951, contemporaneously with the first BR standard Class 5s from Derby. They quickly showed that they were very different machines from their 20 predecessors. They were strong, perhaps stronger than the piston valve engines, and were regarded by some as worthy of being in Class 6, for gone was the sluggishness at low speeds of the earlier engines. Some of the sweetness in running also seemed to have been lost at the same time, though not enough to cause any complaint. But on one occasion No 44686 (I think) *did* cause some bitter complaint with riding very roughly, immediately after repair at Horwich. John Lawson, the CME HQ mechanical inspector with responsibilities for the Caprotti's, had a really wild ride on her on the 'Pines Express' from Birmingham to Crewe; she lurched badly, with a vicious knock, and shouldered her way round curves in violent heaves. After prolonged examination, both at Longsight depot and again in the works at Horwich, a final desperate hunch revealed that there was a differnece of ⁵⁄₈in in diameter of the two driving wheels, due to a gross machining error! When this was rectified, all was sweet reasonableness again.

Another innovation of some importance was the building in 1949 of 10 engines, Nos 44718-44727, with steel fireboxes. These engines were allocated to Scotland where the water was comparatively pure and untreated, and worked mainly between the limits of Glasgow, Perth, Inverness and Aberdeen. These fireboxes were fully welded in the usual way, and stays were screwed and nutted as on copper fireboxes.

Unlike the Bulleid Pacifics, where there was a good deal of cracking of the steel boxes which necessitated welding up and the fitting of inserts at depots,[48] cracking was almost unknown on these Class 5s, and the boxes lasted the life of the engines themselves, nearly 20 years, without difficulty. The main problem which arose was in 'sounding' the stays for breakages, because under the boilermaker's hammer they 'rang' quite differently from stays in a copper box, and gave the impression of being broken when they were (invariably) intact. This led to some furious arguments between boilersmiths and boiler inspectors, quite alarming figures of broken stays being bandied around, only to be disproved.

The last variation, on only six new engines, was the fitting of double blastpipes and chimneys; they were Nos 44755-44757 (Caprotti), Nos 44765/6 (Walschaerts) and No 44767 (Stephenson). Instead of a single 5⅛in dia blastpipe cap 11in below centreline. Two 3¾in dia caps were used (7% greater area) 12in below centreline; on the Caprotti engines the caps were 3⅝in dia. The chimney chokes were moved up 1¾in also. The results obtained will be discussed in the next chapter.

As was usual in the circumstances, there were a number of retrospective modifications made to the 'Jubilees' and Class 5s in the light of experience. Most of these were comparatively minor, but two are worth some attention, one being very substantial and the other, though of a minor nature, with important consequences.

Frame Fractures

Early in World War 2 the incidence of fatigue fractures of 1in thick frames on Class 5s, at the coupled axle horngaps, was becoming so serious that a special investigation into causes and remedial measures was commissioned from the Research Department. As R. C. Bond, then Works Manager at Crewe, commented on receipt of the first interim report on this investigation late in 1943:

'It is ... a good thing that the behaviour of the Class 5 4-6-0 has been concentrated upon ... because although they are not at the moment the worst engines we have to deal with, they are rapidly becoming so ... '

Measured statistically in terms of cracks per engine per 10 years, the Class 5s notched up 3.0 cracks, and were classed as 'bad', while the 'Jubilees' were classed as 'fair' at 1.2 (though it was puzzling that the very similar 'Patriots' had less than half this figure).

Appendix 1 sets out the factors which were considered, with particular reference to the Class 5s. As a result the frame design progressively improved, by incorporating:

— thicker plates (first $1\frac{1}{16}$in, later $1\frac{1}{8}$in),
— hornblocks on leading and driving axles in place of separate axlebox guides (from No 5472 onwards),

— pin-jointed cross-stays at all coupled axle positions, and
— 'Horwich' type hornstays bolted direct to the frame legs.

In addition, for repair purposes a technique was developed of welding in large new inserts to replace cracked material, keeping the welds away from highly stressed areas. This ensured that new material would run a further initial period of at least five years before any cracking occurred. In 1949, I. C. Forsyth, then Works Manager at Crewe, claimed[49] that this was achieving accuracy of frame length, after fitting new full-depth sections, of the order of .003in or better.

Inside Big Ends

The inside big ends on the 'Jubilees' followed standard LMS practice, being of the strap type fitted to the connecting rod with through bolts. Oil from the well in the strap was fed to, and distributed over, the bearing surface by three felt oilpads, of essentially rectangular form 3in long and set transversely in the brasses; the upper one rested in a through slot, half in each brass, which was $5\frac{3}{8}$in wide. These big ends were stripped for examination every 10-12,000 miles, and unless reassembled with care and integrity the seeds of trouble could be sown by the very examination designed to prevent it. (Fig 12.)

At the end of World War 2 and after, with maintenance resources stretched, the incidence of hot inside big ends had become serious on all three and four-cylinder engines, the more so since if not detected in time by the driver, the heated brasses would ultimately disintegrate, and all that remained was a coating of brass dust on everything between the frames. Major and expensive damage usually resulted, either

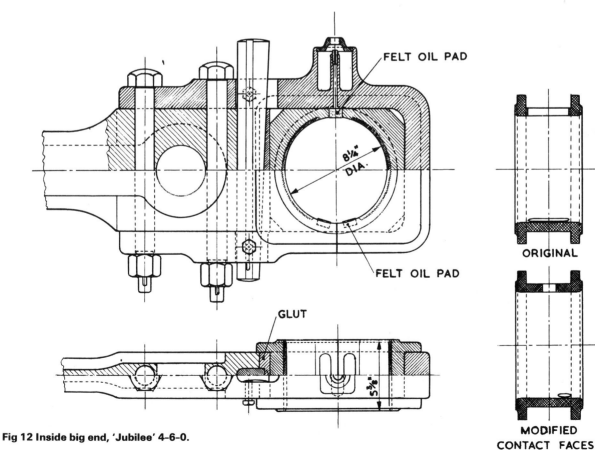

Fig 12 Inside big end, 'Jubilee' 4-6-0.

ORIGINAL

MODIFIED
CONTACT FACES
BETWEEN BRASSES

64

knocking out the front cylinder cover or fracturing the cylinder casting itself; in addition a new big end pin in the crank axle was invariably needed because of brass pentration and brutal bruising by the strap and cotter.

'Stink bombs', designed to release a strong smell of garlic (some said almonds — chacun à son gout!) when the bearing heated, were fitted in holes in the end of the crank pin, but were seldom effective. Many were never smelt even when they operated correctly, and often the post-heating damage had destroyed the evidence of the original cause. However, a few big ends *were* caught in the early stages of heating, and a

common feature was looseness of the brasses due to fretting and deformation of the very small contact faces either side of the top pad, allowing oil to be lost round the pad.

To overcome this weakness, the oil pads were changed to a circular form, about $1\frac{1}{2}$in diameter, staggered across the journal while leaving full contact 'feet' on the brasses. The locking arrangements for the main cotter were also changed, to eliminate any temptation to slacken the main cotter fractionally in order to firm up the locking cotter in it. These changes effectively put a stop to big end disintegration.

The 'Jubilee' Rebuilds

Above : Starting on the gentle fall from the summit of the Chilterns at Tring, No 5735 *Comet* **sweeps down to Northchurch Tunnel at a good 60mph on the 14–coach Saturday 'Lakes Express' in September 1950.** *E. D. Bruton*

Right: Sister rebuilt 'Jubilee' No 5736 *Phoenix* **is at the head of a miscellany of stock as the 23.35 'Horse & Carriage' from Glasgow trundles into Platform 3 at the old Euston in April 1948.** *E. D. Bruton*

Post-Stanier Modifications

Above right: 'Jubilee' No 45562 has had her leading coupled wheels dropped for attention at Leeds Holbeck, revealing that she has been fitted with manganese steel axlebox liners and Horwich hornclips. The compression spring links are still in position. (1967).
Ian Allan Library

Right: As the fireman damps down the clinker in the ashpit from Class 5 No 5305 at Northwich shed, we can see the Horwich hornclip and a glimpse of the back cottered spring link. *J. H. Cooper-Smith*

Below: Someone has left off the topfeed casing of No 44698 at Perth shed, revealing the new pattern clackbox housing. The LH injector delivery pipe is somewhat flattened at the top bend, by 'attention' from the coal hammer, indicating that the clack had stuck open at some time. Built with a boiler with topfeed on the front barrel ring, she illustrates the haphazard use of sloping throatplate boilers at St Rollox (September 1955).
J. Robertson

Above left: Stephenson valve gear on No 44767. The gear is set at about 50% cutoff in forward gear. Note the double return crank with square attachment to the crank pin — the usual LMS four-stud fastening could not be used for clearance reasons. The operating lever stub for the hopper ashpan doors can be seen behind the driving wheel, in a partly open position. *D. Percival*

Left: Timken cannon leading coupled axlebox for a Class 5, showing the drive takeoff for the British-Caprotti valve gear.
Crown Copyright National Railway Museum, York

Below: Caprotti, plain bearing Class 5 No 44743 rests on Newton Heath shed in October 1959. By this time the original cranked outside steam pipes had been replaced by straight pipes. The mechanical lubricators were driven independently from the driving crankpin.
J. E. Wilkinson

Above: Caprotti, roller bearing example No 44756, with double chimney, sits 'dead' on her home Holbeck shed in April 1962. She still retains the cranked outside steam pipes, and has been fitted with AWS equipment.
G. W. Morrison

Right: Caprotti cambox and reversing gearbox on a Class 5 under construction at Crewe works. With the cambox cover removed, the cams, scroll collars and reversing shaft can be seen, with a glimpse of the camshaft splines and cam followers. The gear is in the full forward position. *BR LM Region*

Above left: One of the final two Caprotti Class 5s No 44686, at Willesden. The actuation steam pipe from the dome regulator is evident, as is the peculiar run of the vacuum train pipe to keep it clear of the cambox area.
G. H. Marsh

Left: The other side of No 44686, at Crewe works in July 1962. The mechanical lubricator drive on these two engines had to be taken from the trailing crankpin.
R. J. Henly

Below: The external Caprotti drive (while looking clumsy) and the rotating-shaft reversing gear considerably simplified the area above the cylinders as compared with the earlier engines. The BR standard steam-operated cylinder cocks with which these engines were built can be seen. The crossheads were standard with the piston valve engines, even to the facing and bolt holes for the Walschaerts crosshead arm.
C. R. L. Coles

LMS Postwar Running

Above: No 5552 *Silver Jubilee*, looking grubby and anything but silver, coasts into Colwyn Bay (actually in June 1948) with the 11.15 Euston-Holyhead.
E. D. Bruton

Right: 'Jubilee' No 5696 *Arethusa*, a Kingmoor engine in LMS postwar black-and-maroon livery, charges the 1 in 176 to Sandridge box with the 17.32 St Pancras-Nottingham, at least 11 coaches, the first being an ex-LNWR Wolverton product. (August 1948). *E. D. Bruton*

Below right: No 5741 *Leinster*, from Bushbury and grimy, lays a smoke trail through Harrow on a Euston-Birmingham express in 1947. The 14-coach train includes at least three articulated twin sets. *Real Photos 24121*

Top: Double chimney 'Jubilee' No 5742 *Connaught* pulls out on to Camden bank and heads for her Bushbury home with the Down 'Midlander' express.
Eric Treacy/P. B. Whitehouse collection

Below: Nearly-new Class 5 No 4774 is in charge of the 16.00 FF2 express freight from Carlisle to Masborough passing Gargrave.
Eric Treacy/P. B. Whitehouse collection

Above right: No 4785 piloting 'Jubilee' No 5701 *Conqueror* are hard at work on a Glasgow–Liverpool and Manchester express approaching Uddingston, to rush the bank to Motherwell, in 1947. *Real Photos 24080*

Right: An eight-coach Up express on the S&DJ line comes over the hump to Stalbridge station, in charge of Class 5 No 4830, at that time oil-fired. The Whitaker automatic tablet exchange apparatus, clamped to the tender handrail, is extended ready to pick up the tablet for the section to Templecombe No 2. *Real Photos 15302*

Below: Upperby Class 5 No 4905 is 280 miles from home on a Down express freight train passing Kings Langley. *Ian Allan Library*

Above: An Up empty coaching stock train reaches the summit at Druimuachdar, with its lineside marker board, with Class 5 No 4925 working at about 55% cutoff. *C. C. B. Herbert*

Below: No 4986 is attached to a coal-weighing tender and seven-coach Up express as she speeds past Napsbury in March 1948. *E. D. Bruton*

6
The Stanier 4-6-0s in the Postwar World

Recovery from the difficult conditions of wartime was necessarily slow, and the Stanier engines, along with many others, found themselves in a working environment which differed materially from that into which they had been born prewar. While the works throughput was not greatly affected, five main problems arose in varying degree at motive power depots.

1 Buildings and Accommodation
Seldom attractive places in which to work at the best of times, wartime damage and deterioration made working conditions grim at many depots, inevitably affecting the quality of work done and lowering morale.

2 Maintenance Staff
Acute difficulties arose, at a time of over-full employment, in getting suitable artisans, and holding them, against the competition of industrial plants offering better working conditions.

3 Footplate Staff
The general pace of promotion was much more rapid than prewar, there was a high turnover of staff, and the resulting rapid link progression meant less experience for firemen and less opportunity to form a close team relationship with a driver.

4 Servicing Staff
The rough and arduous conditions on the ashpits led to some lowering of work standards, and skimping of ashpan and smokebox cleaning were not infrequently encountered. Cleaning of engines at some depots was practically unheard of.

5 Coal supplies
The availability of large coal suitable for locomotives declined as the proportion mined by mechanised methods increased, and the proportion of slack in the tender increased further due to the degradation inherent in mechanical coaling plants. There were few 4-6-0 turns which used more than 5 tons, and so on the excellent Stanier 9-ton tenders the front half of the bunker was constantly replenished while several tons of unused coal behind weathered for months or years into poor stuff which was hardly fit for firing.

In the immediate postwar years, acceleration of passenger services was impracticable because of a heavy backlog of track maintenance. Heavy expenditure on new locomotives was in no way matched by upgrading of stabling, servicing and maintenance facilities. A vivid illustration of typical locomotive condition in such an environment is provided by the initial examination of four Class 5s picked for tests in 'rundown' condition in 1954. The selected engines, all with manganese-lined axleboxes, had had one General Repair since new; they were:

No	Depot	Miles since last works repair
44964	Saltley	55,223
44985	Kentish Town	45,610
44987	Agecroft	83,500
44988	Blackpool	78,169

As received at Carlisle for the tests,

— all brick arches were in poor condition,
— safety valves were blowing off at pressures well below the nominal 225lb/sq in. (In one case both valves were blowing hard at 185lb.)
— piston valve rings were broken on two engines, making the beat irregular. (In one case a 3in segment of one valve head was broken off)
— most blastpipes had heavy carbon buildups.
— three engines were badly down on the trailing springs, with only $\frac{3}{8}$-$\frac{5}{8}$in clearance above the boxes.

There were many other defects, some of lengthy standing; the Kentish Town engine, for instance, had only 27 superheater elements in 28 flues![50] Certain minimum work had to be carried out before the engines could be tested consistently as 'run-down'.

With nationalisation at the beginning of 1948, the LMS Railway became the LM Region and part of the Scottish Region, under the overall control of the new 'Railway Executive'. R. A. Riddles was appointed as the Member of the Executive for Mechanical and Electrical Engineering, and one of his first actions in this new post was to propose that:

'...comparisons of performance of different standard locomotives in service should be obtained as soon as possible, to serve as a guide in the design of future locomotives'.[51]

As the details of this exercise were worked up, there was no place amongst the express passenger engines for a 'Jubilee', but in the mixed traffic group the Stanier Class 5 was an automatic choice, to be pitted against the LNER Class B1 and GWR 'Hall' 4-6-0s, and the larger Bulleid 'West Country' 4-6-2, which had some features of the then emerging ideas of a Class 5MT Pacific. For gauging reasons the 'Hall' was banned from the LM and Scottish Regions.

The selected routes and agreed loadings for the tests with the mixed traffic engines were:

Dates of Class 5 tests	Region	Route	Agreed loadings, tons		
			Section	Down	Up
1-4 June	LM	St Pancras-Manchester C		310	310
15-18 June	E	Marylebone-Manchester LR		373	373
6-9 July	Sc	Perth-Inverness	Perth-Aviemore	350*	350
			Aviemore-Inverness	255	255
13-16 July	W	Bristol-Plymouth	Bristol-Newton Abbot	420	—
			Newton Abbot-Plymouth	275	—
			Plymouth-Exeter	—	275
			Exeter-Bristol	—	450

* Assisted in rear, Blair Atholl-Dalnaspidal.

The loadings on the Western Region were heavy by comparison with the express passenger engines, while those on the Eastern Region were, curiously, the normal 'Master Cutler' load, normally an 'A3' job and with few stops. On top of this, certain routes suffered severely from temporary speed restrictions for track condition, preventing anything like time-keeping.

The Stanier Class 5s chosen, on the basis of having run 15-20,000 miles since last General Repair, were No 45253 from Llandudno Jc for the English tests, and No 44973 for the Scottish runs. No 45253 had a line 10 boiler with wartime return loop elements, while No 44973 had a line 9 boiler with bifurcated elements. One Kentish Town crew (Driver H. Smith) handled No 45253 on the three routes; on the unfamiliar ones the crew worked for one week, with a pilotman, before the test runs proper. Regrettably, no consistent — if any — guidance was given to the enginemen involved on what was expected of them, and Smith's instinct seemed to be to drive No 45253 to minimise coal consumption regardless of the timetable. In England, Grade 1 South Kirkby Hards were burned, and in Scotland a lower quality Fife coal, with 8% lower calorific value was provided.

No 45253 was found on transfer to Kentish Town to have a quite bad trailing axlebox knock, and was quickly whipped into Derby works for the valves to be reset with full allowance for expansion when hot (Appendix 6). This virtually eliminated the knock, although during the tests on the LM Region the Report says ' . . . considerable vibration set up, and pronounced knock in trailing boxes when gear notched well up'. The use of 16-18% cutoff on easier grades was reported; more fool anyone for doing so with a two-cylinder piston valve engine!

The author went out on a trial run from Derby to York and back after the valves had been reset, with Driver E. Twigg from Derby accompanied by Inspector Smith, and wrote nine years later:[52]

'That was a beautiful engine, No 45253. There was nothing that she could not do. We brought 10 bogies back from York . . . As we waited at Sheffield for the "rightaway", the Inspector said "Now, Ernest, let's see what she'll do". After about 50 yards (Twigg) pulled up the gear to 55%. Up went the regulator handle to the full open position . . . About Heeley, Twigg pulled her up to 48% and there she was left until we dived into Bradway Tunnel.

'With . . . pressure held between 220 and 225lb by partially shutting the damper to stop her blowing off, and water dead steady an inch from the top nut of the gauge glass, we worked the 300-ton train up to a steady 36mph

on the 1 in 100 gradient, passing Dore & Totley in a few seconds over 9min. I calculate that we were turning out about 1,150EDBHP in the process. And the water consumption from York to Derby? It worked out to the very low figure of 21.8 gallons per mile, equal to about 30lb of coal per mile — and to this economy there is no doubt that expert firemanship, high superheat due to an incandescent fire, and skilled driving all contributed.'

Table 17A

Interchange Trials 1948

Power outputs: Class 5 4-6-0s Nos 45253 and 44973

Date	Location	Grade	Speed	DBHP	EDBHP	Cutoff	Boiler Pressure
St Pancras-Manchester							
2 June	Disley Tunnel	132R	36.5	765	990	33	218
Up	Disley	132R	40.9	810	982	38	221
	Braybrook	132R	34.9	855	1,100	36	220
	Desborough North	132R	38.6	873	1,138	36	210
3 June	Kettering Jc	200R	51.7	828	989	29	219
Down		average					
	Haddon	102R	29.8	747	960	36	222
	Gt Longstone	100R	37	880	1,118	36	217
4 June	Chinley South Junction	90R	28.8	932	1,186	47	223
Up							
Marylebone-Manchester							
15 June	Amersham	104R	25.5	693	860	35	220
Down	Annesley	132R	31.5	736	898	38	210
	Penistone	130R	27	796	986	40	215
16 June	Crowden	117R	34.6	998	1,225	45	225
Up	Springwood Tunnel	100R	27	819	1,015	45	215
	Rushcliffe	176R	53.7	940	1,074	38	210
	Ashby Magna	176R	45	945	1,120	38	215
Bristol-Plymouth							
14 July	Silverton	343R	53.5	1,102	1,302	35	218
Up	Hele	306R	60	1,126	1,380	35	212
	Cullompton	155R	56	1,105	1,398	35	214
15 July	Wellington Bank	203R	46.5	939	1,164	35	208
Down	Dainton Bank	36R	26.7	783	1,239	45	216
		65R	32.7	928	1,200	45	213
Perth-Inverness							
6 July	Stanley Jc	125R	44.5	852	1,025	30	230
Down	Carr Bridge	60R	24.6	768	1,068	45	235
7 July	Etteridge	95R	32	902	1,130	37	220
Up	Dalwhinnie	80R	22	843	1,066	50	230
	Druimuachdar	80R	27.9	916	1,160	42	235

R — rising gradient

WR Bristol-Plymouth. The Report notes that: 'Hemerdon bank was climbed on both occasions on a transitory steaming rate . . . Full regulator, 60% cutoff, 12.5mph on 14 July and 15.5mph on 16 July, pull 9.3 tons referred to level on both dates.'

Table 18

Interchange Trials 1948. Marylebone-Manchester, 15 June

Distance Miles		Engine: Load: tare/gross, tons	45253 370/390 Schedule Minutes	Actual Time Min Sec	Speed	Class 5 4-6-0 at 18,000lb/hr water* 390 Calculated Time Min Sec	Speed
0.0	Marylebone		0	0.00	—	0.00	—
5.1	Neasden South Jc		11	10.28	57	8.59	69½
				2×pws			
9.2	Harrow		17	18.34	—	13.22	
				pws			
8.0	Rickmansworth		14	12.47	27*	10.16	58½/25*
12.4	Chalfont		22	22.49	24½ min	18.46	32 min
19.6	Gt Missenden		30	33.40	66/41	27.39	75/67½
				pws			
28.7	Aylesbury		40	45.24	—	36.21	—
8.9	G. Underwood Jc		11	12.01	61½/48	10.44	69½/54½
29.4	Culworth Jc		32	33.40	64½/51/ 67	30.14	70½/55½/73
31.2	Woodford Halse		35	36.24	—	32.29	—
				2 x pws			75 max
14.1	Rugby		17	21.22	—	15.33	
19.9	Leicester		23	24.44	67 max	20.33	75 max
9.9	Loughborough		12	—	—	12.24	75 max
13.5	Nottingham		17	—	—	16.01	75 max
0.0	Sheffield		0	0.00	—	0.00	—
				signal stop			
					30 max	pws	39 max
13.1	Penistone		25	34.37	—	22.57	—
6.0	Dunford Br		13	13.54	—	12.04	37½
23.4	Guide Bridge		37	43.37	—	31.31	65 max

*16,000lb/hr water rate for first 10 min (starting cold)

This was the machine which was entrusted to Driver Smith to put through her paces for the honour of the LM Region.

On the St Pancras-Manchester route, timings were of wartime leisureliness — 121min Down and 119min Up between St Pancras and Leicester, for instance — and yet 10min running time and more was lost on every journey without exception. To anyone brought up to prewar standards, the running was abysmal.[53] Yet it was a cut above what was to come on the Great Central section; there, running time was lost in handsful on each journey, the worst case being 43.8min northbound on the first day.[51]

Table 17A extracts from the official report particular instances of performance considered typical of the working.

There has been so much discussion about the Class 5s showing on the Great Central line, based on opinions rather than facts, that calculations have been made of the running of a BR Standard Class 5 with 373-ton loading from Marylebone to Nottingham, and Sheffield to Guide Bridge, working at a water rate of 18,000lb/hr, and in Table 18 these timings (with no recovery margin) are compared with the actual running on 15 June,[53] the first of No 45253's days on this route. The calculated times demonstrate that there was considerable variability in the timetable, with very slack sections and others rather a counsel of perfection. But the actual speeds really say it all, particularly on the rising gradients. Instead of 32-33½ up to Amersham, 24½-25½. 41 over Dutchlands summit instead of 56½. Beyond Finmere, 48 instead of 54½ topping the 1 in 176, and 51 before Helmdon rather than 55½. No more than 30 on the climb to Penistone instead of 39. The downhill running was equally desultory; on the racing ground from Ashby Magna to Leicester, where prewar 'B17s' regularly came down at 85-90, nothing over 67. Only

in the Up direction was the engine called upon to exert herself.

Much of the Class 5 interest centred on the Bristol-Plymouth trains. One can only suppose that in the month following his GC line performances, Driver Smith had been 'suitably spoken to' by someone in authority in the light of the dynamometer car records, because suddenly the combination of Smith and No 45253 came to life. Table 19 shows details of his work from Exeter to Bristol on 14 July;[53] the selected power outputs[51] for the first time lay in the 1,200-1,400EDBHP range.

Not very much is recorded about No 44973's running, except that she steamed freely and was generally worked with the regulator fully open and with cutoffs of 35-50% on the heavy grades — typical Highland driving methods. The safety valves were found to be blowing off at 235lb/sq in, incidentally, but were not changed; a little extra 'kick' was always welcome on this road!

The coal and water consumptions for the two Stanier Class 5s for the whole series of tests were as follows:

	45253		44973
	St Pancras-Manchester	Marylebone-Manchester	Bristol-Plymouth	Perth-Inverness
Coal: lb/mile	38.1	40.5	39.2	48.3
lb/DBHP hr	3.71	3.29	3.39	3.90
lb/sq ft grate/hr	58.1	54.5	60.8	58.7
Water: gal/mile	29.4	32.1	30.4	40.0
lb/DBHP hr	28.6	26.1	26.3	32.3
Evaporation: lb/lb coal	7.70	7.93	7.77	8.27

Taken over the whole series of tests with the mixed traffic engines, and bearing in mind that the 'Hall' only ran on two of them, the various contestants compared in efficiency thus:

	Coal lb/DBHP hr	Water lb/DBHP hr
LM Class 5 4-6-0	3.54	28.0
ER Class B1 4-6-0	3.59	27.6
WR 'Hall' class 4-6-0	3.94	30.0
SR 'West Country' 4-6-2	4.11	32.6

The marginally lower specific coal consumption of the Stanier engine as compared with the 'B1' was well within the 'scatter' to be expected in such trials, and was not significant.

The Report on the Interchange Trials came to nine conclusions. They are hardly worth repeating, even in summary, for they could all have been written beforehand. The entire test series really proved nothing and was more or less valueless for its declared purpose.

In July and August of the following year, a series of dynamometer car tests was conducted on the St Pancras-Manchester route to compare the coal and water consumptions of various Class 5 developments. The same loading of 310 tons was laid down, the trains being on 'Limited Load' timings. The engines selected for the comparison all had roller bearings on all axles and line 9 boilers and were:

No 44757 with Caprotti valve gear and double chimney. The camboxes had been fitted with solid exhaust cams just prior to selection for the tests.
No 44764 with Walschaerts valve gear and standard single chimney.
No 44766 with Walschaerts valve gear and double chimney.
No 44767 with Stephenson valve gear and double chimney.

As in 1948, Grade 1 South Kirkby Barnsley Hards were fired, although the Stephenson engine apparently got an inferior batch with slightly lower calorific value.

Dynamometer Car Report No 94 shows that the manning of the test runs was not ideal; no less than three sets of Trafford Park men worked the test trains with each engine during its four-day trial, and there were marked variations in working methods and firemanship. Steaming was of very mixed standard, and only No 44757 (Caprotti) was 'very

Table 19
Interchange Trials 1948. 13.35 Plymouth-Bristol, 14 July
Engine: Class 5 4-6-0 No 45253
Load: tons tare/gross 447/475

Distance Miles		Schedule Minutes	Actual time Min Sec	Speed
0.0	Exeter St Davids	0	0.00	—
3.4	Stoke Canon		6.26	49
7.2	Silverton		10.51	53/57
12.6	Cullompton		16.16	61½/55
14.9	Tiverton Jc		18.36	62
19.9	Whiteball		24.09	52
			pws	30
23.7	Wellington		28.48	72
30.8	Taunton	38	36.44	—
2.4	Creech Jc	4	4.30	50½
5.8	Durston		8.17	57
11.6	Bridgwater		14.03	64
17.9	Highbridge	20	19.58	65/64
25.1	Uphill Jc	28	26.55	66
32.8	Yatton		33.51	71
36.7	Nailsea		37.20	66
38.9	Flax Bourton		39.22	58
41.6	Long Ashton		42.00	64
44.8	Bristol Temple Meads	53	46.50	—

satisfactory throughout'. No 44766 had problems and pressure fell to 175lb/sq in at St Albans on the first day. With No 44767 (Stephenson) steaming was very free on two days with one crew, whereas with the other crews, on the first day pressure was down to 170lb/sq in at Flitwick and on the last day there was 'some mismanagement of the fire'. On one day, thanks to skilled handling, No 44764 recorded a coal consumption as low as 3.06lb/DBHP hr.

Timekeeping was not good, not least because of a plethora of signal checks on top of up to five permanent way slacks. The running of No 44764 was largely ruined by these delays, and the Report could only observe laconically that 'sectional timekeeping was ... *well within the capacity* of the four engines tested'. My italics! Recorded steam temperatures were interesting in that the piston valve engines averaged 590-610°F (660°F maximum), whereas the Caprotti engine consistently bettered these figures by 40° or so. This was attributed to the 3⅝in blastpipe caps on No 44757, but the difference seems too great to be due to this alone.

Coal and water consumptions were:

	44757	44764	44766	44767
Coal: lb/mile	34.5*	34.8	33.8	34.5
lb/DBHP hr	3.36*	3.39	3.55	3.52
lb/sq ft grate/hr	55.6*	54.9	53.7	54.3
Water: gal/mile	27.0*	28.5	28.9	26.9
lb/DBHP hr	26.4*	27.7	30.3	27.4
Evaporation: lb/lb coal	7.85*	8.18	8.53	7.78

*Coal and water consumptions on 5 July omitted due to failure of exhaust steam injector.

For each engine there was a fairly consistent and expected pattern of lower specific coal and water consumptions with harder work.

The Report drew the following conclusions from these tests:

' ... there is no marked difference in the coal and water consumptions of the four engines tested'.
' ... the Caprotti engine was stronger in the gear, at earlier cut-offs, than the other engines ... otherwise there was no great difference in the general performance'.

In 1950 and 1951 three series of tests were run at the Rugby Testing Station, looking into:

Variations in valve lead	No 45218 January-May 1950
Efficacy of single and double chimneys	No 44765 June-October 1950
Clean and dirty boilers	No 44862 1951

The second of these was specific to the Class 5s following the fitting of double blastpipes to six engines in 1947/8, but the remainder merely used them as convenient guineapigs.

For the variation in lead tests, the valve heads were successively modified to provide leads from $\frac{1}{16}$in to $\frac{5}{16}$in in $\frac{1}{16}$in steps, while retaining the $\frac{1}{16}$in exhaust clearance. The cutoff was maintained constant against the lead changes by adjusting the reversing screw, the corollary being slight changes in the release and compression events. The valves were set in accordance with the latest LM practice, pulling both heads back $\frac{1}{32}$in when cold from the nominal $\frac{1}{4}$in leads. This practice, developed from the author's work in 1948 to eliminate axlebox knock[52] (see Appendix 6), was stated in Rugby Testing Station Report R2 as:

'to equalise the work done in the front and back ends of the cylinders, to prevent excessive compression in the front ends, and to improve the riding'.

In fact, the valves, if properly set for hot conditions, produced these benefits without further adjustment.

The findings of this test series can be summarised thus:

1 At speed, increase in lead gives more power, although more than $\frac{1}{4}$in lead gives little or no increase. Leads of less than $\frac{1}{8}$in result in serious loss of power. At low speeds the effect is negligible.
(This contrasts oddly with the results of the lead tests on 5653).
2 $\frac{1}{8}$in and $\frac{3}{16}$in leads gave the lowest coal consumption.
3 At 60mph, there was a 3.5% coal consumption advantage when working with full regulator and 15 and 20% cutoffs as compared with part regulator and cutoffs 10% longer to give the same power, though at higher outputs this advantage disappeared.
4 Vibration was worse with $\frac{1}{16}$in and $\frac{5}{16}$in leads than at intermediate values.

The report concluded that:

'... $\frac{3}{16}$in lead gives the lowest consumptions for most conditions of passenger train working but ... $\frac{1}{8}$in lead is slightly better for low speeds'.

Coal consumption was not the important criterion, however, and no alteration was made to the Class 5s nor was the advice taken for the BR standard engines.

As a bonus, the steam and gas temperatures for No 45218's line 5 boiler were noted over a wide working range, and as Fig 13 shows, the increasingly upward tendency was distinctly curious, since it is more normal for the temperature characteristic to droop as output increases.

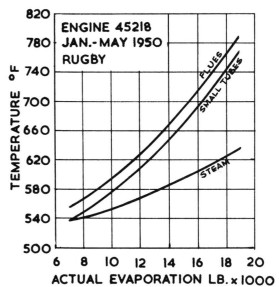

Fig 13 Steam and gas temperatures, Class 5 No 45218, 1950.

No 44765 now went to Rugby for draughting tests, including the effects of chimney taper. Clearly the Swindon influence was being felt through the Locomotive Testing Committee! No 44765 carried the line 9 boiler, the draughting proportions being as in Fig 14. The standard single blastpipe and chimney had proved themselves over many years, and there was no call to juggle with blastpipe and choke sizes or positions, which had been such a feature of the prewar 'Jubilee' tests. All that was done by way of modifying the chimneys was to insert liners, springing from the chokes, with a taper of 1 in 14 à la Swindon, and extended to the full height permitted by the loading gauge.

The engine was tested over a wide range of speeds (25-75mph) and cut-offs (15-45%), giving evaporation rates with Grade 1 South Kirkby coal from 8,000lb to more than 24,000lb/hr of steam, and wheel rim HP's from under 600 to

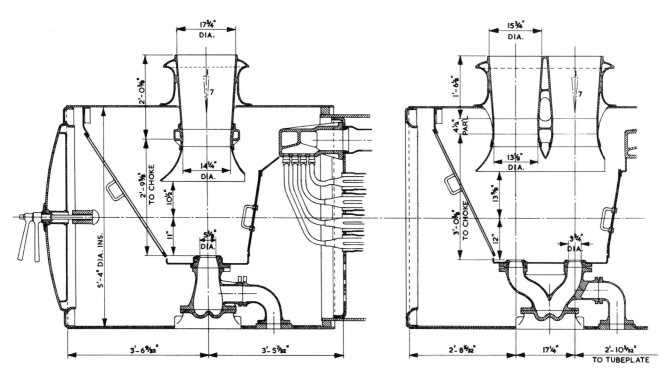

Fig 14 Blastpipe and chimney arrangements, Class 5 No 44765.

more than 1,500. Report R3 covering these tests comments interestingly that:-

' . . . to obtain the maximum possible rate of evaporation it was found necessary to limit the speed to 40mph, as any attempt to run faster at the very high power output involved resulted in slipping of the engine on the rollers. This is characteristic of two-cylinder engines with a high percentage of the reciprocating masses balanced'.

(By this time new Class 5s had reverted to the original practice of balancing 66% of reciprocating masses).
The findings of the tests were:

1 The exhaust pressure below the double blastpipe caps was consistently only 82% of that for the single blast-pipe over the whole working range.
2 The smokebox vacua produced by the standard single, and double, blastpipes was not materially different, though the double blastpipe was less effective up to about 15,000lb/hr steam rate but produced the higher vacuum above this figure (Fig 15).
3 The linered single chimney produced about 11% more draught than the standard one at any given steam rate (Fig 15).

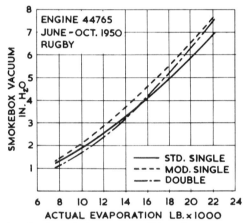

Fig 15 Graph of smokebox vacuum/blastpipe pressure, Class 5 No 44765.

4 'To prevent this increased draught from raising the . . . excess air unduly it was necessary to reduce the damper openings, the damper control being more critical . . . For the very highest rates . . . it was also found beneficial, if not essential, for additional air to be admitted above the fire, both to improve the combustion and to reduce the very heavy loss of unburnt fuel.' Subject to these adjust-ments the boiler was steamed up to a maximum evaporation of 24,750lb/hr. However, it must be said that these subtleties in air control were almost certainly outwith the skills and comprehension of most firemen.
5 The linering of the double chimney produced less than $2\frac{1}{2}$% improvement in draught, and the remarks in 4 above applied though in lesser degree.

The gas and steam temperatures over the working range are shown on Fig 16. The report drew attention to the fact that:

'The temperature of the gas leaving the small tubes is higher than that leaving the flues at all firing rates, con-trary to earlier results with the 21-element boiler,'

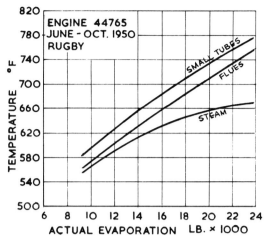

Fig 16 Steam and gas temperatures, Class 5 No 44765.

as shown in the tests on No 45218, though in view of various differences in design this was not significant. The final con-clusion drawn was that no change in the standard Class 5 single chimney draughting could be justified, and this was the deathknell for the double chimneys when renewals were required.

In this report the first reference is made to human frailty, in the form of a note that the highest rates of evaporation were:

' . . . far above anything that the fireman had ever experi-enced and the duration of the tests had to be appreciably curtailed on the grounds of human endurance.'

Such tests normally occupied about 40-45min plus build-up period. In fact, quite early at the Rugby plant it was found that the use of the nearest-in-time spare fireman from Rugby depot produced an unacceptable 'scatter' of results, and it was ultimately agreed to make two specified firemen of high competence available for stationary testing work, both being used when maximum output tests were made.

In 1951, Class 5 No 44862 was tested at Rugby with, first, its boiler dirty and then with a newly overhauled boiler of the same type, the remainder of the engine being unaltered in condition. The results were hardly very significant; provided that tubes and flues were clean, boiler output was little affected by normal scaling, etc, on the water side.

Finally we come to the tests in 'run-down' condition, to which I have alluded in Chapter 5. The four selected engines were tested in comparison with No 44981, fresh from General Repair and in 'as-new' condition, over the G&SW route between Carlisle and Hurlford, using the Mobile Testing Plant units, and were at constant steam rates with each engine, the train being run in steps of constant speed at each rate.

Report L99 of December 1954 summarises the results thus:

'At comparable tender feed rates, the average 'run-down' engine gives 50-110HP less at the drawbar than the 'new' engine . . . this represents some 10% deficiency.
' . . . in the case of engine No 44988 with broken piston valve head and rings, this deficiency was approximately 20% in the middle of the range of speeds and steam rates.'

On boiler performance, however, the position was rather different:

'The relationship between coal fired and feed water evaporated was sensibly the same for engines in 'run-down' and 'new' conditions alike.

'... the boiler front-end limit of the 'new' engine was 22,000lb/hr water. Two of the 'run-down' engines (44985 from Kentish Town and No 44988 from Blackpool) maintained rates of approximately 20,000lb/hr for a test period of adequate duration, whilst a third engine (No 44964 from Saltley) appeared to be capable of maintaining this rate after the boiler had been washed out and the tubes cleaned. Before washout the maximum rate was not greatly in excess of 16,000lb/hr ... It appeared ... that provided the tubes were clean, 'run-down' condition did not materially affect the maximum evaporative capacity ...'

though the superheat temperature tended to be about 20°F lower.

The penalty was thus predominantly in the use, rather than the generation, of steam.

While this variety of testing had been going on, the real railway was still at work and was slowly pulling itself back from wartime conditions and their aftermath towards something more like the standards of prewar. This was not to become, with steam traction, ever quite like 1939 when the LMS was operating 68 runs daily, totalling 6,902 miles, at 60mph and over. In 1955 the equivalent figure was 2,114 miles, and even by the summer of 1958 this had not reached more than 43 runs totalling 4,116 miles daily.

Chronologically this is the moment to mention an amusing, yet potentially deadly serious, incident in the summer of 1952. The author received a phone call in mid-morning from the Divisional Motive Power office at Derby to the effect that a bogie wheel *had just dropped off* No 45654 on Holbeck shed. Though it was some months after 1 April, some convincing was needed before setting off for Leeds to examine the casualty. But it was genuine enough; the engine had worked an overnight express from St Pancras to Sheffield and the 07.12 stopping train thence to Leeds, and at 10.10, approaching the Holbeck coaling plant on a gentle left-hand curve, the left leading bogie wheel had fallen off and lay flat on the ground alongside! Examination showed a creeping fatigue flaw in the axle at the bossface, starting from a stress-raiser caused by faulty machining of the journal radius, which had spread with increasing rapidity until it took up about 70% of the cross-section of the axle before the final crystalline break. It was an ex-'Claughton' pair of wheels, dating from a 1917 build, and the axle made from Crewe steel, one of quite a few such wheelsets in use on 'Jubilees'.

By 1953, however, the magic words 'XL Limit' were reappearing in the Working Timetable, though on the LM Region this was confined in the summer timetable to five trains on the Euston-Birmingham line, which the Bushbury 'Jubilees' ran in great style within their load limit of 350

Table 20
Euston-Coventry

		Loco No	45742						45737			
		Load, bogies	10						11			
		tons tare	314						350			
		tons gross	335						380			
		Enginemen	Not recorded						J. Bird (Bushbury)			

Distance Miles		Schedule Minute	Actual Time Min	Actual Time Sec	Speed	Boiler pressure	Regulator	Cutoff	Schedule Minute	Actual Time Min	Actual Time Sec	Speed
0.0	Euston	0	0.00		—	220	$2/5$	60/30	0	0.00		—
5.4	Willesden Jc	10	9.12		55	210	$2/5$	25	9	9.19		—
8.1	Wembley		12.00		61		$2/5$	25		11.50		67
11.4	Harrow		15.12		61		$2/5$	25		14.48		—
13.3	Hatch End		17.07		60½	210	$2/5$	27		16.39		64
17.5	Watford Jc	22	21.01		70		$2/5$	25/18	23	20.23		—
21.0	Kings Langley		23.59		71	220	$2/5$	18		23.23		70
24.5	Hemel Hempstead		27.04		69	225	$2/5$	18		26.30		—
28.0	Berkhamsted		30.09		67		$2/5$	20		29.46		—
31.7	Tring	36	33.41		63	215	$2/5$	18/15	35	33.19		62
36.1	Cheddington		37.23		73		Shut	—		36.50		—
				pws	35	225	$2/5$	25				
40.2	Leighton Buzzard		42.13		—		$2/5$	20		39.44		88
46.7	Bletchley	49	47.50		74/70		$2/5$	15/17	47	44.24		—
52.4	Wolverton		52.27		78	220	$2/5$	17		48.39		—
54.8	Castlethorpe		54.32		74		$2/5$	17		50.27		—
				pws			Shut	—				
59.9	Roade	60	59.23		64/25		$2/5$	28	58	54.45		70
62.8	Blisworth	63	63.25		64		$2/5$	25	61	57.14		—
69.7	Weedon	69	69.31		71	225	$2/5$	18/20	67	62.39		75
75.3	Welton		74.22		64		$2/5$	22/15		67.15		66
80.3	Hillmorton		78.50		74		Shut	—		71.36		—
82.6	Rugby	81	80.55		50*	225	$2/5$	20	79	73.57		*
89.1	Brandon & W.		87.13		75		$2/5$	22	③	81.23		—
94.0	Coventry	93	92.06		—		Shut	—	94	86.57		—
	Net Time:		88¼min									

*Permanent speed restriction
③ Recovery time

tons. Table 20 sets out two Down runs on these trains. The first was a footplate trip which I made in that first summer on the 14.20 Euston-Wolverhampton train, with the (then) double chimney 'Jubilee' No 45742. The 10-coach load was 314 tons tare, so that we could have taken another coach if necessary within the limit. The engine was worked quite easily, mostly with the main valve of the regulator just a little open and with running cutoffs in the 15-25% range. Steaming was excellent, though the draught was very keen on the rear portion of the grate with the back damper fully open, and there was some tendency to throw fire which became very noticeable in tunnels. There was no steam chest pressure gauge on these engines, but from experience with the two rebuilt 'Royal Scots' so fitted I would estimate that steam chest pressures would be between 165 and 185lb/sq in. Water consumption through to Birmingham was at a rate of 32.8gal/mile, equivalent to about 43-44lb/mile of coal. I estimate that power output was about 985EDBHP at Hatch End and just a shade over 1,000 to Tring. The whole thing was done with consummate ease by the Bushbury crew.

The second run in this table[54] needed considerably harder work; the train was the 18.55 Euston-Wolverhampton, loaded right up to the permitted limit, and again with a Bushbury crew. The speeds up to Hatch End (64 minimum) and Tring (62 minimum) with this load were very good indeed, representing about 1,170 and 1,120EDBHP respect-

Table 21

14.30 Birmingham New St-Euston, November 1956
Locomotive: Class 6P 4-6-0 No 45601 *British Guiana*
Load: coaches 9
          tons tare/gross 310/330
Enginemen: Not recorded

Distance Miles		Schedule Minutes	Actual Time Min	Probable Speeds
0.0	Birmingham New Street	0	0	
18.9	Coventry	21	19¼	
11.4	Rugby	17	14	
12.9	Weedon	13	—	80
19.8	Blisworth	19	19½	
22.7	Roade	22	—	Over 70
30.2	Wolverton		27¾	80
35.9	Bletchley	33	32	
50.9	Tring	48	—	65
65.1	Watford Jc	60	55¼	Over 80
77.2	Willesden Jc	71	65	Over 80
82.6	Euston	79	73¾	

ively, and the subsequent 88 before Leighton Buzzard and an average of 81.7mph thence to Castlethorpe on well-nigh level road shows no lack of steam. Likewise the minima of 70 over Roade and 66 at Kilsby were of a very high order. As a result there was a net gain on schedule of 4min to Coventry, the Wembley-Hillmorton stretch being run at an average speed

Table 22

Leicester-St Pancras

	Loco No:		45598		45614	
	Load: bogies		10		10	
	tons tare		354		325	
	tons gross		375		355	
	Driver & Depot:		Not recorded		Bailey (K. Town)	
Distance Miles		Schedule Minutes	Actual Time Min Sec	Speed	Actual Time Min Sec	Speed
0.0	Leicester	0	0.00	—	0.00	—
3.7	Wigston		6.43	*	6.18	54*
9.4	Kibworth North		—	57	12.02	60½/58
12.8	East Langton		15.46	74	14.58	81½
16.2	Market Harborough	19	18.31	55*	17.44	57*
20.6	Desborough North		—	52	22.52	48
24.5	Glendon South Jc		—	—	26.22	75½
					pws	27
27.1	Kettering	31	29.42	75	29.09	—
28.5	Kettering Jc		pws	30	—	—
30.9	Finedon		—	74	33.22	70
34.1	Wellingborough	37	36.47	60*/65	36.07	70*/65½
39.4	mp 59¾	43	42.37	44	41.13	50
46.1	Oakley	48	48.47	79/72	46.43	82½/70
47.4	Oakley Jc		sigs	37	—	—
49.2	Bedford	51	52.22	—	49.13†	78½
55.3	Millbrook		pws	45	—	—
57.3	Ampthill		61.53	51	56.06	61
58.9	Flitwick		—	56	57.37	64
61.8	Harlington		67.12	—	60.28	59½
66.3	Leagrave		72.05	52	65.06	55½/61
68.9	Luton	70	74.22	71	67.22	72/68
74.5	Harpenden		79.05	74	72.08	72/70
79.2	St Albans	79	82.53	75	76.03	74
83.9	Radlett		85.22	79	79.42	80
86.7	Elstree		88.37	67	82.00	67
92.2	Hendon	90	93.05	80	86.22	79½
			sigs			
99.1	St Pancras	99	104.52	—	93.50	—
	Net Times		96min		92min	

*Permanent speed restriction
†Time at Bedford North Jc

of 72.5mph. This was a better performance than anything done under dynamometer car conditions on these trains during the 1930s.

A major effort in the reverse direction, late in 1956, was unfortunately recorded in outline only, but is set out in Table 21.[55] With a load one coach under the 'XL Limit' allowance, No 45601 was put to making up a 6min late start from Birmingham. The engine had recently had a General Repair at which she had shed her domeless straight throatplate boiler and gained another to either line 9 or 10. Excellent work was done to the stops at Coventry and Rugby, where station overtime unfortunately made the train nearly 2min late leaving. There then followed some extremely fleet running to Euston, with an average speed from Blisworth to Willesden of some 75-76mph, giving an arrival $3\frac{1}{2}$min early.

The reintroduction of 'XL Limit' timings to the Midland Division began very tentatively in the summer of 1954 with a single train, and made little headway until the winter timetable of 1956 brought a massive acceleration between London and Derby/Nottingham. Now 18 trains daily notched up 1,266 miles at 60mph and over, start-to-stop. The 'Jubilees' and many of their crews took this as a spur to produce performances ranking with the finest for engines of this size, and often better than prewar. The two runs from Leicester to St Pancras in Table 22 have been selected as the worst cases of overloading from a total of 13 published runs made during the second half of 1957 and 1958, seven of which took loads of over 300 tons unassisted. Yet *in every case* there were actual or net gains on the 99min schedule, ranging from $2\frac{1}{4}$ to $14\frac{1}{2}$min. On the other hand, it must be freely admitted that the 13 runs were the cream, and not a representative sample of performance; in other cases there was some rather dismal running, and piloting because of the 300 ton limit was all too frequent.

The first run,[56] on the 10.25 from Manchester, had a rather brutal loading for a 'Jubilee' on this route of 354 tons, though what made the 10-coach train quite so heavy is not known. The short climbs to Kibworth North, at a sustained 57, and to Desborough North, falling only from 55 to 52, both required a little over 1,500EDBHP and would have needed something near 40% cutoff and a steam rate of 28,000lb/hr for short periods. Clearly the boiler was having to be mortaged heavily, and the maximum of 74mph at East Langton and the modest average of 61.7mph from Desborough down to Kettering show that little or no steam was being given downhill. This was good enginemanship, however, with the load and timetable in mind. A lesser effort was made up to Sharnbrook Summit, and the fireman may well have welcomed the Bedford signal check to get his boiler into shape for the long pull up to mp 34. Nevertheless, a sound climb was made, at a minimum of 52mph and involving about 1,140EDBHP, and the train would have arrived in St Pancras only about $1\frac{3}{4}$min late, had signal checks not intervened in the closing stages. But a net time of 96min reflects superb enginemanship with 354 tons, and it is a great pity that it cannot be credited to the men concerned.

The second run[57] was on the Up 'Palatine Express', with that stalwart *Leeward Islands* in the very able hands of a Kentish Town crew. There was no slacking in the start from Leicester, but from the Great Glen dip up $1\frac{1}{2}$ miles of 1 in 156/161 to Kibworth North the engine was really hammered to drop no more than from $60\frac{1}{2}$ to 58, requiring briefly about 1,450EDBHP. From the Market Harborough slack up to Desborough North the work was nearly as forceful, needing something like 1,300EDBHP. Driver Bailey was evidently getting a little time in hand for the permanent way slack near Kettering. Thereafter, a fine climb to mp 34, with speed falling only from $59\frac{1}{2}$ to $55\frac{1}{2}$ on the last $3\frac{1}{2}$ miles of 1 in 200, assured an early arrival. The calculated EDBHP above Harlington was about 1,160, and net time was 7min inside schedule.

Whatever steaming troubles they may have had in the hands of some men, the 'Jubilees' were always very fleet of foot, helped by the substantial lead giving large port openings at short cutoffs, and this was frequently demonstrated on the Midland, notably on the 1 in 200 down from Leagrave to Bedford, and in the Up direction on the slightly steeper falls to the Radlett dip and to Hendon. Well-authenticated speeds in the 90's were fairly commonplace, but the highest I have been able to trace was with an unidentified engine[58] on a train of 308 tons northbound, when 96 was reached at Flitwick and, after a drop to 92 on the flatter two miles to Ampthill, a further 95 before easing for the Bedford curve.

Examination of Midland running is a reminder of an incident, probably in 1956, involving a pair of 'Jubilees' and which well and truly blotted Newton Heath's copybook. A full-blown Royal Train was to be worked after the Grand National from Aintree to St Pancras, via Manchester Victoria, Marple, Peak Forest and Derby. It was fully recognised that water would need to be watched carefully, for the first opportunity to replenish the tanks would be at Loughborough troughs, over 100 miles from Aintree. Newton Heath and Bank Hall engines with 4,000gal tenders were selected, and turned out in immaculate condition after a most meticulous examination including gauging the water pickup scoops. Newton Heath men relieved Bank Hall crews at Manchester to work through to London. The Midland Division authorities were asked to specially ensure that Loughborough troughs were brimming over, for they were not the fastest of fillers.

But come the night, with tanks very low, and another train just ahead had scooped Loughborough nearly dry, and by the time both engines had dipped in turn they had picked up less than 1,000gal apiece. No way were they going to make Oakley troughs, 59 miles further on. After a hasty consultation between the drivers by sign language, in the dark, it was decided that there was no alternative but to get water at Leicester station. So with all signals off, they stopped in Platform 3 and filled the tender of each engine in turn, a 10min unscheduled halt, in the unguarded platform. The top operating brass on the train were hopping up and down wondering why steam locomotives could not run without water. The recriminations went on for weeks, and the two drivers would not have been surprised if they had been arraigned for treason!

For anyone seeking a picture of the footplate scene on a hard-worked 'Jubilee', as seen through the eyes of an experienced fireman, I can hardly do better than refer to Terry Essery's vivid description of a trip[59] from Gloucester to Birmingham on the night Mail in the mid-1950s. No doubts there about his ability to produce steam against *both* injectors, albeit on a fairly short-term basis, even when the working of the engine was brutal.

Would that all 'Jubilee' work had been to such standards; in February 1955 the Chief Operating and Motive Power Officer at BR HQ persuaded the Locomotive Testing Joint Committee that their steaming needed to be improved. The subsequent report of the tests, from the Rugby Testing Station (Report R11) commented in its preamble:

'... they form a very important section of the motive power available ... on the London Midland Region and in particular of the Midland Division ... on important routes of which they are the largest express locomotives now running ...
'For some time past these engines have been the cause of considerable anxiety ... because of poor steaming. Never the best of steamers, even in prewar conditions, the present fuel situation has accentuated their troubles to an extent that is causing difficulty in operation'.

If this was indeed the considered view of the senior operating officers, one can only marvel that they should be planning an accelerated service on the Midland Division which was 'Jubilee'-based, and detect a certain readiness to unload the problem on to the CME rather than to put their own house in order. In so doing they ignored the proven capacity of the engines prewar, the standards currently being set by many enginemen, the causes of indifferent enginemanship, and the whole question of getting coal of the right quality into the tenders of engines on important work.

It is relevant to recount a contemporary personal experience with Newton Heath-based 'Jubilees' which used an alternative approach. In the mid-1950s this large Manchester depot, with an allocation of about 160 loco-motives, had 10 'Jubilees' to cover a daily Glasgow diagram and a variety of shorter Central Division express turns. The 16.15 Manchester-Glasgow and 10.50 return (the times varied a little over the years) were 'Limited Load' trains on which 'Jubilees' were allowed — and invariably got — 365 tons north of Carnforth on start-to-stop timings of:-

		Down		Up	
Miles		Min	Av Speed	Min	Av Speed
21.0	Preston			25	50.4
19.1	Lancaster	101	53.5	20	57.3
49.9	Oxenholme Carlisle			74	40.5
73.5	Carstairs	93	47.4	78	56.5

The trains were worked by a small 'Glasgow Link' of eight sets of men as a lodging turn, the drivers being senior men in the link progression, although the firemen were volunteers side-stepping the normal progression for two years at a stage where their experience of hard continuous running was limited.

Considerable care was taken with maintenance, servicing and the cleaning of the Newton Heath 'Jubilees', and performance on the Glasgow trains was watched intently. The firing instructor, George Sleight, put in many days on them, particularly when the firemen changed. Nevertheless the timekeeping of the Down train especially was deplorable, culminating in *average* late arrivals in Glasgow in November and December 1957 of 28 and 45min respectively, though only a very small proportion could be unambiguously laid at the door of engines or men. All normal efforts seemed unavailing in rectifying this situation. 'Royal Scots' were just not available, and we had no better men.

The *basic* trouble was diagnosed as one of morale (the ramifications of which spread into many related fields, together with a need for firm attention to — ie greater involvement in — the 'trivia' of the engines' working cycle. The 'Jubilee' diagrams were linked, and in some cases broken

down — much to the chagrin of the Divisional office — to enable three designated engines in first class order to be dedicated to repetitive weekly programmes, so arranged that some legitimate but short out-and-home runs to Leeds, Blackpool and Southport were made between Glasgow trips, to avoid the engines becoming 'lost' and also (very important) to empty the tender. The weekly programmes specified in detail the daily routine — when each engine was to get her washout/'X'-day or 'Boiler Full' exam, when she would be cleaned (including the cab interior), tubes blown through, and coaled. Instead of topping up the bunker every time the engine came on shed, as usual, it was arranged that on return from Glasgow a gang of cleaners was put into the tender to shovel all residual coal forward for use on the first fill-in trip. Thus every man in the Glasgow link knew in advance which engine he would have, that it would be in good mechanical order with paintwork gleaming, and that the tender would be full of nothing but Grade 1 coal. No 45671 *Prince Rupert* in particular was turned out at this time virtually to Royal Train standard, with the motion burnished in fancy patterns. And the result? Within two weeks the 16.15 train was consistently right time *or early* into Glasgow, and the crews were like the proverbial dogs with two tails. I relate this episode only to illustrate an important facet of steam locomotive work which was all too often forgotten; when an engine was required to work regularly near its limit, the climate had to be created that generated such effort, both with men and machine. After World War 2 it needed all the skills of management to produce such a climate.

So to No 45722 on the Rugby plant. Her boiler was to line 17, with postwar $1\frac{3}{8}$in dia return loop elements, which reduced the free gas area to only 14.0% of the grate area. With standard draughting the front end limit was found to be at a steam rate of 20,760lb/hr using 3,324lb/hr of Blidworth Grade 2B coal; pro-rata to calorific value South Kirkby Grade 1 would probably have produced about 22,500lb/hr. Now No 45722 as tested was nominally identical with No 5660 *Rooke* during her 1937 dynamometer car trial, with the sole exception of those $1\frac{3}{8}$in elements. The significance of the reduction in free gas area and the increased gas flow resistance in the superheater does not appear to have been

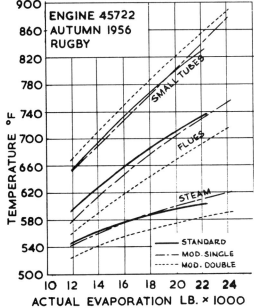

Fig 17 Steam and gas temperatures, Class 6P No 45722.

appreciated at the time, but the effects soon became apparent from the results. The recorded temperatures in the smokebox opposite large and small tubes, and of the superheated steam, are shown in Fig 17; the starvation of the flues led to steam temperatures barely reaching 600°F at maximum output. Yet in the 1946 tests with No 5733 the $1\frac{1}{4}$in dia return tube elements had produced temperatures in the 620-630°F range as normal, with a maximum of 670° on one occasion, while No 5740 in 1937 produced similar figures. At the same time the increased superheater resistance was diverting more gas through the small tubes, giving very high smokebox temperatures opposite them. Clearly No 45722 was not living up to previous standards.

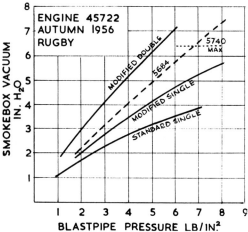

Fig 18 Graph of smokebox vacuum/blastpipe pressure, Class 6P No 45722.

The relationship between smokebox vacuum and blastpipe pressure was also right out of line with what had been established during prewar tests. Fig 18 compares the Rugby results with those obtained with Nos 5684 and 5653 in 1937 which, despite differences in tubeplate layout and blastpipe diameter and height, produced reasonably consistent results which left No 45722 standing. The conclusion must be drawn that not only had the boiler been downgraded by the superheater alteration, but that the draughting of this particular engine was below par. A black sheep indeed! (See Appendix 8.)

Improvement to the draughting took two alternative forms, a revised single blastpipe and chimney, and an equivalent double combination. At this time the Swindon star was at its zenith in the testing firmament, and they had recently evolved the concept of a sharp-edged orifice blastpipe instead of the usual internally tapered cap, contrary to all previous practice. In this application the orifice was $5\frac{1}{8}$in dia[60] and was teamed up with an altered chimney with $14\frac{1}{2}$in choke and 1 in 14 taper. The double chimney was based on one made for trial on a rebuilt 'Royal Scot' but not adopted, and two sharp-edged blastpipe caps $4\frac{1}{8}$in dia were used, giving 12.5% more area than the single orifice.

On test the revised single chimney arrangement raised the front end limit with Blidworth coal from 20,760lb/hr to 24,500lb/hr and at the same time produced better combustion; the standard arrangement was unable to induce enough gas flow to provide adequate excess air at high outputs. The double chimney produced a maximum of 26,000lb/hr of steam, again with improved combustion. Opening out the orifices to $4\frac{3}{16}$in reduced the limit to 25,000lb/hr. A further graph in the report purported to show 'the highest steaming rates that could be *relied* upon in daily

service with the existing and the modified front ends...' With Blidworth coal the original draughting was credited with a peak of 15,000lb/hr, and for the modified front end 19,000lb/hr. It claimed that:

'...at ordinary express speeds the potential power output... had been increased by one third'.

The new blastpipes had curious effects on temperatures and gas flow. As Fig 17 shows, the abnormally high temperature differential opposite large and small tubes with the original draughting (90°F at 20,000lb/hr steam rate) was not significantly altered by the Swindon single chimney, whereas the double chimney depressed the large tube temperature and raised that opposite the small tubes, increasing the differential to 154°F at this rate. This was probably due to the abnormally low position of the chimney choke and bellmouth relative to the tube bank, and the absence of deflector plates. The preferential draughting of the small tubes, and a lower firebox temperature with more secondary air, pulled the steam temperature down by 20-25°F, which could only be detrimental. The sensitivity of combustion conditions to correct damper opening was increased, as in the case of the Class 5 No 44765.

The report also drew attention to the build-up of carbon in the sharp-edged orifices, a new feature, since the standard blastpipe was only cleaned at 30-36,000 miles:

'The orifice type of cap is more sensitive... as the carbon tends to build up as a lip, curved upwards, which forms in effect a small nozzle instead of a sharp-edged orifice. It is necessary that such orifices should be cleaned at fairly frequent intervals... The double blastpipe arrangement is more sensitive than the single... because the caps are smaller... If (the Motive Power Department) are prepared to ensure that the caps are cleaned at every boiler washout then an orifice of $4\frac{3}{16}$in diameter is recommended, but if the intervals... are likely to be much longer, then $4\frac{1}{8}$in diameter should be used...'

It is a great pity that this latter information was not passed down to depot level. In the spring of 1958, No 45702 came back to Newton Heath from Crewe works fitted with the modified single blastpipe and chimney; she was immediately allocated to one of the Glasgow programmes. Imagine the dismay, then, when reports from drivers, backed by the firing instructor, said that No 45702 was certainly no better than the other engines in the roster, and that steaming noticeably deteriorated as she approached washout. After steam and water testing, we had to find by experience that the performance 'fade' was due to carbon build-up in the blastpipe cap. After that it was cleaned out at every washout (12-16 days), but even then there was no detectable benefit in steaming.

Finally, it was remarked that:

'At rates of steaming approaching their present front end limit these locomotives eject a large quantity of sparks from their chimneys. The modified chimneys have done nothing to reduce this spark throwing but have made it much easier for the engines to work at rates at which this is serious. This feature may need watching...'

thus aggravating a common trait with the 'Jubilees' and which had been very marked with the keen 'Kylchap' blastpipe on No 5684, and to a lesser extent with the double chimney on No 45742.

The report made no clearcut recommendations, but offered the prospect that:

'... either of the two modifications of the chimneys and blastpipes will achieve a very marked increase in the potential power output of locomotives of this class and also enable them to use lower grade coal than at present without failure becoming probable ...'

Would that this could have been demonstrated in traffic, but this was not the case.

To sum up the No 45722 tests, therefore, it may be said that:

1 The boiler proportions, always a little on a knife edge, had already been unbalanced by the postwar superheater element modification.

2 The standard blastpipe and chimney tested appear to have been below standard and unrepresentative.

3 The redesigned Swindon draughting restored the boiler to its prewar capability, though at the expense of superheat and other characteristics, and making it very sensitive to correct air control.

4 The new design did not meet the needs of the Motive Power Department.

5 The tests were not taken far enough to produce an optimum draughting design or to mitigate the lurking weakness of inadequate free gas area.

The latter point could have been largely overcome by using the Class 5 28-element tubeplate, as Appendix 8 illustrates. Unfortunately, with time running out it was too late to indulge in major boiler modifications. A total of 10 'Jubilees' was fitted with the modified single blastpipe and chimney during 1957/8, but the double blastpipe was removed from No 45722 and was not reproduced on any other engine.

Let us now turn to postwar Class 5 running, and since so little of what has been published was recorded from the footplate, it may be appropriate to establish a yardstick for comparison by describing a run the author made in 1958 which in some ways may be regarded as typical of their day-to-day work, though in other respects it was far from being so. The train was the 10.25 Manchester Central-St Pancras, on 'Special Limit' timings on which a Class 5 was allowed 275 tons over the Peak. It was November, and Manchester was swathed in one of those dense pea-soup fogs for which, pre-Clean Air Act, it was notorious. As we ran down to Throstle Nest East Junction it was so bad that we could barely see the front buffer beam, and after a yellow at the colour-light distant we crawled down to the semaphore outer home at less than walking pace; if it had been 'on' it is doubtful whether we could have stopped without a slight overrun. It also made for a terribly greasy rail which caused some slipping, but after Cheadle Heath the fog became patchy and we emerged from Dove Holes Tunnel into clear sunshine — a not uncommon phenomenon. The load was two coaches under the limit.

Table 23

10.25 Manchester Central-St Pancras

Locomotive: Class 5 4-6-0 45279
Load: coaches 6
        tons tare/gross 203/215
Enginemen: Dvr W. Richards, Fmn Cox (Trafford Park)

Distance Miles		Schedule Minutes	Actual Time Min Sec	Speed	BP	Reg	Cutoff
0.0	Manchester Central	0	0.00	—	225	FV	25
			slipping signals	2			
1.5	Throstle Nest East Jc	4	6.49	—	220	FV	25
			slipping				
	Chorlton Jc		10.10	43/54	—	$\frac{1}{2}$	25
8.0	Cheadle Heath	13	15.15	52/54	225	$\frac{1}{2}$	30
			pws				
	Bramhall Moor Lane		18.44	46/30	215	Full	35
12.0	Hazel Grove		21.14	42	—	Full	35
			slipping				
15.2	Disley		—	40/51	215	Full	35
17.0	New Mills South Jc	26	28.12	—	215	Full	35
19.7	Chinley	31	32.20	44/-	—	—	—
2.0	Chapel-en-le-Frith		4.32	37	220	Full	35/40/35
5.7	Peak Forest	11	10.09	41	210	FV	32
10.3	Millers Dale	17	15.04	—	—	—	—
2.7	Monsal Dale		4.06	65/64	210	Full/FV	42/30/22
6.4	Bakewell		7.23	70	—	Shut	—
9.8	Rowsley	12	10.21	52*	225	Full	30
14.2	Matlock	17	14.40	—	—	—	—
	Whatstandwell		—	66/54*	225/210	Full/$\frac{3}{4}$	35/25
6.8	Ambergate	9	8.23	59/30*	215	Full	30
			signals,	slight			
11.9	Duffield		13.25	64	210	Full	30
			signals,	slight			
17.2	Derby	20	18.36	80/-	205	—	—

Net Time, Manchester-Chinley 26½min
*Permanent speed restriction
Water consumption: 2,200gal=35.7gal/mile

The engine was in fine shape, and the work of Fireman Cox was excellent — a medium thick fire, incandescent, fed sparingly, mainly in the back corners and under the door. Table 23 shows that up through Dove Holes Tunnel speed was gradually worked up to 41mph, the EDBHP being about 1,060. Once over the top, driver Richards gave the engine her head where the road allowed. Unusual was the acceleration from 52 at the Rowsley curve slack to 76 before the Matlock stop, with full regulator and 30% cutoff even at this speed, and the same treatment after the Ambergate station slack, from 30 up to a full 80 before shutting off for Derby. This is relevant to what will be said about the run in Table 29 later. Water consumption was 2,200gal, or 35.7gal/mile.

Table 24

The 'Palatine' express, Manchester Central-St Pancras
Locomotive: Class 5 4-6-0 No 44985
Load: coaches 8
    tons tare/gross 260/275
Enginemen: Dvr Winston (Kentish Town)

Distance Miles		Schedule Minutes	Actual Time Min Sec	Speed
0.0	Leicester	0	0.00	—
3.7	Wigston		5.55	45*
9.4	Kibworth North		11.43	62½/63
12.8	East Langton		14.27	83
			signals	50
16.2	Market Harborough	19	17.24	53*
20.6	Desborough North		22.18	54½
24.5	Glendon South Jc		25.40	76½
			signals	38
27.1	Kettering	31	28.18	—
34.1	Wellingborough	37	35.02	68½/65*
36.4	Irchester		37.10	63
39.4	mp 59¾	43	40.02	59½
46.1	Oakley	48	45.10	88½/80
49.2	Bedford North Jc	51	47.27	81½
54.1	mp 45		51.23	67½
57.3	Ampthill		54.19	64
58.9	Flitwick		55.48	67½
61.8	Harlington		58.28	62½
65.1	mp 34		—	60 min
68.9	Luton	70	65.03	73/65/70
74.5	Harpenden		70.00	66½/68/66
79.2	St Albans	79	74.01	75
83.9	Radlett		77.22	87½
86.7	Elstree		79.37	67
92.2	Hendon	90	83.59	83/68
97.6	Kentish Town	96	88.30	70/67
99.1	St Pancras	99	90.48	—

Net Time: 89min
*Permanent Speed Restriction

At this time Class 5s were very much playing second fiddle to the 'Jubilees', but they could certainly rise to almost any occasion. Table 24 details a run[61] on the Leicester-St Pancras leg of the through 'Palatine Express' working from Manchester, with a load up to the 'XL Limit', and run in a net time of 89min, the actual gain on schedule being 8¼min. The downhill work was fast, even though 90 was nowhere reached. But the uphill work was truly magnificent, both in the short, hard effort on the early climbs and the sustained work, albeit at a lower level, on the long pull up to mp 34. Note the *acceleration* from 62½ at Great Glen up 1 in 156/161 to 63 at Kibworth North — needing about 1,380EDBHP — and similarly from 53 through the Market Harborough slack up 1 in 132 to 54½ at Desborough North — about 1,300EDBHP. Over 2½ miles up 1 in 120 from Irchester to Sharnbrook Summit caused no greater drop in

speed than from 63 to 59½ — something like 1,480EDBHP — and over mp 34, nothing less than 60mph after 15min of sustained hard work at up to 1,070EDBHP. Driver Winston of Kentish Town and his unrecorded fireman could be proud of their day's work.

Table 25

17.15 Aberdeen-Glasgow (Buchanan Street)
Locomotive: Class 5 4-6-0 No 45115
Load: coaches 7
    tons tare/gross 248/265
Enginemen: Not recorded (Ferryhill)

Distance Miles		Schedule Minutes	Actual Time Min Sec	Speed
0.0	Forfar	0	0.00	—
5.7	Glamis		6.25	74
7.9	Eassie		8.04	80
12.0	Alyth Jc	12	11.11	77
16.7	Coupar Angus		15.01	78/65
18.9	Burrelton		16.55	72
21.2	Cargill		18.52	82
25.3	Stanley Jc	23	21.59	75
28.3	Luncarty		24.22	78
			Signals	
32.5	Perth	31	30.58	—

Net time: 27½min

No study of Class 5 performance can overlook the Scottish contribution; indeed, one wonders what to leave out rather than what to include. Observers of locomotive performance will hardly need reminding of the Up Aberdeen Postal, for instance, with its tight timings even in the immediate postwar years. But some of the finest Class 5 running was made working turn-and-turn-about with the 'A4s' on the three-hour Glasgow-Aberdeen trains. In 1962-64 the timekeeping of these trains was not impeccable, but almost none of the loss could be laid to 'locomotive running', apart from a perennial problem of overtime taking water at Perth. The Stanier Class 5s were in no way inferior to the 'A4s' on these trains. So it is part of a run on the 17.15 Aberdeen-Glasgow, over the level racing ground from Forfar to Perth with a straight-throatplate engine in charge of Ferryhill men, which has been selected to show what they could do by way of sustained fast running[62] (Table 25). Incidentally, Ferryhill men had been in separate LMS and LNE links until the 1950s, but a merger was then made and LNE men found themselves handling Class 5s and LMS men driving 'A4s'. Each developed a healthy respect for the others' machines.

One hardly thinks of the Highland main line as one where high speeds are to be expected, but the run in Table 26 shows that it *could* happen.[63] A 5min late start from Aviemore was enough to trigger off this piece of exuberance. An average speed of 48mph start-to-stop, including getting up to 1,315ft above sea-level at Slochd, mostly on single line with 40mph restrictions through the crossing loops — which were taken in somewhat cavalier fashion, admittedly — was quite remarkable. The EDBHP on the 1 in 60/70 climb to Slochd Crossing is estimated at about 1,250, with the engine driven on full regulator and about 45% cutoff.

One of the most remarkable climbs from Carlisle to the summit at Ais Gill must have been that in the next run, the more so because of the difficult circumstances in which it was made, and the fact that it took place during the twilight of steam. The train was a relief to the Up 'Waverley Express'

Table 26
16.25 Glasgow (Buchanan Street)-Inverness

Locomotive: Class 5 4-6-0 No 44798
Load: coaches 7
        tons tare/gross 242/255
Enginemen: Not recorded

Distance Miles		Schedule Minutes	Actual Time Min Sec	Speed
0.0	Aviemore	0	0.00	—
—	Top of 1 in 150		—	52/44
6.5	Carr Bridge	10	9.13	56
—	Top of 1 in 60		—	32½
11.8	Slochd Crossing	21	17.58	35/67
15.5	Tomatin	26	23.12	35½*/64
19.6	Moy	31	27.43	44*/66
23.6	Daviot	36	31.58	53*/74
27.8	Culloden Moor		36.00 signals	60*/79½
33.9	Millburn Jc	47	41.28	10
34.4	Inverness	49	43.33	—

Net Time: 43min
*Permanent Speed Restriction

Griseburn box speed was allowed to tail away to 44. But then the engine was opened up to some purpose; the easier grades to Smardale Viaduct produced 59mph, 2½ miles of 1 in 100 thence brought speed no lower than 50, and 47 after a further 2¼ miles of the same grade. On the easier mile at Mallerstang speed recovered to 54, and then on the renewed 1 in 100 there was a further acceleration to 56, but there was a gradual fall to a minimum of 52½, probably due to pressure drop. But this performance required about 1,290EDBHP, and power had been sustained at over 1,200 for at least 12 minutes.

For comparison, in this Table I have also shown a run[65] with one of the Caprotti Class 5s, which to say the least were not the preferred engines on this difficult line. This was another relief train, this time from Glasgow, and the engine probably came on fresh at Carlisle. O. S. Nock commented:

'... the start out of Carlisle was no more than moderate. But on the brief downhill stretch to Armathwaite the engine got rapidly into speed, and a very hot pace was then sustained ...'

from Edinburgh, and had been badly delayed by engine failure at Hawick. Class 5 No 45028, another straight throatplate engine, came on cold at Carlisle after a long wait which could not have improved the fire, and the train was then further delayed by a freight train as far as Lazonby. So the restart from Appleby was 58min late, and here Table 27 takes up the story.[64]

O. S. Nock at the time spoke of a 'not particularly vigorous start', and on the 1 in 100 from Ormside up to

How typical of Caprotti work, Nos 44686/7 excepted. No 44757 got a good run at the main climb from 68 at Ormside. Nevertheless, the climbing to Ais Gill could have been bettered almost as a matter of course by a piston valve engine, for speed fell rapidly on the 1 in 100 sections. The summit was breasted at a minimum of 44mph (about 1,020EDBHP). Higher than usual speeds down from Blea Moor had the train through Hellifield in less than 2min over 'even time', which was creditable over this route.

Table 27
Carlisle-Hellifield

Locomotive: Load: coaches tons tare/gross Enginemen:		Class 5 4-6-0 No 45028 7 229/235 Not recorded			Class 5 4-6-0 No 44757* 7 230/240 Not recorded		
Distance Miles		Schedule Minutes	Actual Time Min Sec	Speed	Schedule Minutes	Actual Time Min Sec	Speed
0.0	Carlisle				0	0.00	—
0.9	Petteril Bridge Jc					2.45	28
2.7	Scotby					5.52	37
6.8	Cotehill					11.40	48/44
8.3	Low House					13.43	61
9.9	Armathwaite					15.20	53/64
13.0	mp 295					18.27	57
19.7	Langwathby					24.06	62
15.4	Lazonby				19	20.37	72/68
23.3	Culgaith					27.40 pws	68 55
27.8	Long Marton					31.53	61
30.8	Appleby	0	0.00	—	36	35.02	50
33.2	Ormside		4.10	56½		37.35	68
36.1	Griseburn		7.44	44		40.35	51
38.2	Crosby Garrett		10.31	53		42.58	57
40.0	mp 268		12.21	59		—	62
41.4	Kirkby Stephen		14.00	50/51		46.23	50
44.8	Mallerstang		17.59	47/54		50.38	43/50
46.0	mp 262		19.23	56		—	—
48.3	Ais Gill	24	21.51	52½	59	55.12	44
51.4	Garsdale		24.45	72/64		58.12	70/61
59.6	Blea Moor	36	31.57	72/63	70	65.41	72/62
65.5	Horton-in-Ribblesdale		37.00	75/70		70.16	83
73.5	Settle Jc	47	43.31	76	84	75.58	88
76.8	Hellifield	51	47.04	—	87†	78.28†	70/68

*Caprotti valve gear
†Passing times

If anyone needed to be convinced that the Class 5 was an outstandingly fine engine, probably enough has been said already to do so. But it is the superlative, rather than the outstanding, which shows just what breeding can do. For this purpose I will conclude with just two more runs, the first of which (within the last two years of steam in Britain) shows that high speed capability had by no means suffered from the run-down in maintenance, while the second produced a new high — albeit short — in absolute power output.

The undulating line from Chester to Shrewsbury acquired a reputation in the last days of steam for energetic running and high speeds, particularly in the Up direction, and Table 28 records a run of spectacularly high speed as late as 1966.[66] The crew was from Shrewsbury, and the load no more than 204 tons tare. The start from Gobowen was not particularly fast — contemporary running was producing

Table 28

Chester-Gobowen-Shrewsbury
Locomotive: Class 5 4-6-0 No 44917
Load: coaches 7
      tons tare/gross 250/265
Enginemen: Not recorded (Shrewsbury)

Distance Miles		Schedule Minutes	Actual Time Min Sec	Speed
0.0	Gobowen	0	0.00	—
1.8	Whittington		3.03	66
4.8	Rednal		5.29	82/84
6.3	Haughton		6.36	84/96*
10.5	Baschurch		9.30	92/88
14.3	Leaton		12.01	88/90
18.0	Shrewsbury	18	16.15	—

*See text

times 20sec faster to Rednal — but by this time the driver was piling on everything he had. Speed on the mile of 1 in 240/136 rising past Rednal was held at 84, and the subsequent two miles down at 1 in 132/178 past Haughton was claimed to have produced a maximum of 96. This is, however, unsubstantiated by the passing times, and analysis of theoretical performance at brief very high steaming rates suggests that the engine could not have reached more than 93. The rising grades to Baschurch caused no greater fall than to 88, and 90 was reached again before shutting off for Shrewsbury. The *average* speed over the 9.5 miles from Rednal to Leaton was 87.2mph! No 44917, the engine concerned, was withdrawn only 12 months later!

Finally, sheer cylinder output. On 8 May 1963 the 10.15 Glasgow Buchanan St-Aberdeen train made the running set out in Table 29.[67] The start was badly affected by out-of-course delays, but after Larbert, with a clear road, an unprecedented performance was put up on Kinbuck bank, followed by a very fast run across the tableland to Gleneagles and down to Perth. A veil was drawn over the observance of the 40mph restriction through Stirling station, justifiably, but Kinbuck bank itself, 4.6 miles mainly at 1 in 100/88 but with short stretches both steeper and flatter, was taken at a minimum of 58mph, involving an EDBHP of about 1,800.[68] This would be equivalent to a steam rate of over 31,000lb/hr.

Subsequent correspondence in the magazine *Railway World* suggested[69] that this performance would be impossible with a single Class 5, and it was reported that this train often took an assisting engine working back unbalanced to Perth,

Table 29

10.15 Glasgow (Buchanan Street)-Aberdeen
Locomotive: Class 5 4-6-0 No 44970
Load: coaches 7
      tons tare/gross 250/265
Enginemen: Not recorded

Distance Miles		Schedule Minutes	Actual Time Min Sec	Speed
0.0	Glasgow (Buchanan St)	0	0.00	—
			Sig stop pws etc	
22.1	Larbert	31	34.40	*
24.3	Alloa Jc	34	37.00	75
26.1	Plean		38.26	68
27.8	Bannockburn		39.53	78
30.2	Stirling	41	42.01	*
32.0	Cornton Siding		43.54	72
33.1	Bridge of Allan		44.48	72
35.1	Dunblane	47	46.43	60/58
37.8	Kinbuck		49.22	62
45.2	Blackford		55.22	82/75
			pws	30
47.4	Gleneagles	62	58.07	—
49.5	Auchterarder		60.14	70/87
59.3	Forgandenny		67.30	89/85
61.2	Hilton Jc	74	68.54	*
63.2	Perth	78	72.07	—

Net Time: 63min
*Permanent Speed Restriction

which fact must have been overlooked. In all the circumstances this seemed most unlikely in this case. So it was necessary to verify whether a really all-out effort, well beyond the continuous capacity of the boiler, could have produced such running. By extrapolation, at this steam rate, the calculated speeds would have been:

	Actual recorded speed	Calculated speed
Cornton Siding	72	72
Bridge of Allan	72	68½
mp 122¾ (top of 1 in 100)	—	63½
Dunblane	60	62
mp 125¼ (top of 1 in 84)	58	57
Kinbuck	62	60

This is quite near enough for purposes of comparison; this output, sustained for 6min, could have been produced with pressure held steady while the water level dropped just over 3in — half a glass. Cutoffs would have been in the 40-45% range.

Just what motivation existed for such an effort will never be known, but cutoffs of over 40% at 60mph constitute thrashing with a vengeance! Yet if there are any lingering doubts as to its feasibility, look back to Table 23 and its full regulator, 30% cutoff working at speeds up to 80mph. Only another turn on the reversing screw and you are on No 44970 roaring through the woods below Dunblane and alongside the meandering stream on the line from Kinbuck. Oh yes, it could be done all right! And I am in no doubt that it was.

The south end of the West Coast Main Line

Above left: Double chimney 'Jubilee' No 45742 *Connaught* is in charge of the Down 'Midlander', here seen heading for Primrose Hill Tunnel in July 1951. She has made a quick turnround at Euston, and coal is out of sight in the tender, presumably thanks to trimming by the fireman.
E. R. Wethersett/Real Photos 24244

Left: Fresh from General Repair in 1956, Class 5 No 44771 is working easily as she passes Kilburn No 1 on the Down slow line with empty vans.
Real Photos 24189

Below: Early Class 5 No 45025, now preserved at Aviemore, ambles through Kensington Olympia on a transfer freight from the Southern Region to Willesden in 1951. *E. D. Bruton*

Above: Rugby-based No 45150 accelerates hard on to Bushey troughs to get water, after a dead stand for signals in the station, on the 06.40 Wolverhampton-Euston in 1951.
E. D. Bruton

Right: In the leafy cutting leading to Watford Tunnel, No 45005 makes music on a Euston-Blackpool relief train in 1949. She has been wrongly fitted with a standard top-feed cover instead of the mock 'dome' used on the domeless boilers.
E. R. Wethersett/Real Photos 24246

Below right: 'Jubilee' No 45605 *Solomon Islands* darkens the sky south of Rugby as she accelerated an Up parcels train towards Kilsby Tunnel in 1958. Clifton Road Junction box, closed in 1939, was perched above the Down Northampton line behind the tender.
P. H. Groom

Birmingham New Street

Above: Double chimney Bushbury 'Jubilee' No 45742
Connaught starts the Sunday 10.30 Wolverhampton-Euston
from the gloom of the old New St station in September 1953.
E. D. Bruton

Below: Class 5 No 44870 pulls into New St station in 1955 with
a Down express.   *C. P. Boocock*

North Wales

Above right: No 44686, one of the last two Caprotti Class 5s, and in 1962 allocated to Llandudno Junction, whisks an eight-coach Euston-Llandudno express along the main line through Prestatyn. *Derek Cross*

Right: Still shiny from a General Repair and repaint, earlier Caprotti Class 5 No 44740 coasts into Llandudno Junction on a Manchester-Holyhead boat train in 1960. *Derek Cross*

Below: Conway Castle watches as an Up parcels train, headed by No 45003, penetrates its walls in 1964. *Derek Cross*

Into Central Wales

Above: It's lunchtime as Class 5 No 45147 pulls into Whitchurch with an express freight from the Shrewsbury line, while a BR standard 2-6-4T potters about. *G. H. Marsh*

Below: Unusually, it is 'Jubilee' No 45577 *Bengal* rather than a Class 5, working a light three-coach train from Shrewsbury to Swansea in 1964, here seen near Knucklas. *Derek Cross*

Above: Knucklas station offers no traffic for a Swansea-Shrewsbury train pulling in behind No 45190 in 1964.
Derek Cross

Below: Three miles further on, the same train waits at Knighton while the fireman hangs on to the chain of the water tank.
Derek Cross

Northwards from Crewe

Left: Class 5 No 44685 has taken water from Moore troughs and pitches into the climb to the Manchester Ship Canal bridge at Acton Grange Junction, south of Warrington, with a Down fitted freight in 1958. The formation of the original line, abandoned when the Ship Canal was built, can be seen beyond the tracks. *T. Lewis*

Below: Double chimney 'Jubilee' No 45596 *Bahamas* accelerates a fully fitted Crewe-Carlisle freight past Springs Branch (Wigan) ready for the severe pull up to Boars Head, in March 1962.
J. R. Carter

Below: Sparkling in May sunshine, No 45621 *Northern Rhodesia* rounds the curve from the West Coast main line at Morecambe South Junction with a Raleigh charter special (one of 11 that day) from Nottingham in 1952.   *E. D. Bruton*

Bottom: Crewe-based 'Jubilee' No 45679 *Armada* pulls out of St Bees with the 10.50 Workington-Euston in 1960.   *J. L. Boyd*

The Fell Country — Grayrigg and Shap

Above: The 'Lakes Express' carried portions from Windermere and Keswick, combining at Oxenholme. Here 'Jubilee' No 45738 *Samson*, a grubby Upperby engine, draws the seven-coach Windermere section out of the branch platform at Oxenholme to set back on to the Keswick five coaches in the Up main platform, in July 1960. *T. Boustead*

Left: Loaded up to the 365-ton limit on the afternoon Liverpool and Manchester-Glasgow express, No 45698 *Mars* attacks Grayrigg bank just above Oxenholme in August 1964. She had only 14 months to live. *Derek Cross*

Below left: The banking engine will drop off the rear of this Down through freight at Grayrigg any moment now, leaving Class 5 No 45329 to work the train the level five miles to Tebay and another banker up to Shap Summit. *Ivo Peters*

97

Above right: Watering the milk! The fireman on 'Jubilee' No 45593 *Kolhapur* was slow in getting his scoop out of Dillicar troughs while working a Carlisle-Staverton milk special on Whit Monday 1952. *E. D. Bruton*

Right: Class 5 No 44907 rolls along the Lune Gorge at the head of the 13.55 Carlisle-Edge Hill express freight in June 1952. *E. D. Bruton*

Below: A sunny morning on the Cumbrian fells finds Class 5 No 44790 hammering away on the 1 in 75 towards Scout Green box with a very mixed freight, helped in rear by one of Tebay's parallel boiler 2-6-4Ts.
W. J. V. Anderson

Above: On the 1 in 125 and round the reverse curves at Bessie Ghyll, No 45368 is working hard on an Up through freight.
W. J. V. Anderson

Left: Gently blowing off and with sanders on, double chimney No 45596 *Bahamas* gets a Keswick Convention special away from Penrith for the south, over a tortuous path from the Down loop platform in July 1962. The first two coaches are an articulated twin, and there is at least one more such pair in the train. *Derek Cross*

Below left: On a reverse curve at Plumpton, an Easter Crewe-Glasgow relief express speeds down to Carlisle behind Class 5 No 44987.
Derek Cross

The Midland Line in the Home Counties

Above: An Up express emerges from the darkness of Elstree Tunnel into dappled September light as Class 5 No 44777 pilots 'Jubilee' No 45667 *Jellicoe* over the last 11 miles into St Pancras (1953).
E. R. Wethersett/Real Photos 24251

Right: No 45612 Jamaica, from Kentish Town, is pulling hard on the 1 in 200 from Radlett up to Elstree with the 09.04 Sheffield–St Pancras in the Autumn of 1952. The side of the narrow 3,500gal tender is unusually lined. *E. D. Bruton*

Below right: Morning sees the overnight sleeping car express from Edinburgh Waverley, running late, near Napsbury in charge of a well-polished No 45659 *Drake*, with two loaded milk tanks behind the tender (1951).
E. D. Bruton

Above left: It's Rugby Cup Final Day, 1952, at Wembley, and Featherstone Rovers supporters are relying on Class 5 No 45104, a well turned-out Newton Heath engine seen here at Sundon, to get them to the match on time. *E. D. Bruton*

Left: Nearly at the top of the long 1 in 200 climb from Bedford to mp 34, the 08.04 Sheffield-St Pancras, 10 coaches behind 'Jubilee' No 45594 *Bhopal*, overtakes an '8F' on the slow line at Sundon box in 1952. *E. D. Bruton*

Below: The afternoon Cricklewood-Derby empty milk tanks are seen here breasting the summit at Desborough behind double chimney Caprotti Class 5 No 44756 in 1949. *A. F. Taylor*

The Yorkshire Heartland

Below: Bristol's Caprotti Class 5 No 44743 is coasting into Sheffield Midland station in charge of the 14.12 Bristol-York in May 1952. *E. D. Bruton*

Bottom: A late-1950s scene at Leeds City as 'Jubilee' No 45608 *Gibraltar* pulls out with the 11-coach 'Devonian'. She has acquired a BR Standard chimney. *K. Field*

The 'Long Drag'

Above: Starting the descent from Blea Moor, the fireman of No 45013 can sit down and admire the Pennine views as his pick-up freight passes Ribblehead station, with Batty Moss Viaduct in the background.
Eric Treacy/P. B. Whitehouse collection

Left: With a white feather at the safety valves, No 45593 *Kolhapur* speeds past Dent with the 10.17 Leeds-Glasgow in July 1967, just three months before withdrawal — and preservation. *Paul Riley*

Above: 'Jubilee' No 45568 *Western Australia* seems to have things well under control as she breasts Ais Gill summit in July 1962 on an Up express. *C. P. Boocock*

Below: Near the same spot, No 45573 *Newfoundland* has had her last firing for a while as she comes up towards the summit on a Gourock-Leicester CTAC Scottish Tours special in July 1965. *M. S. Burns*

Lickey and Farther West

Above: Still carrying her chrome-plated cabside numbers, No 45552 *Silver Jubilee* is nearing Blackwell on a northbound through freight in 1964, also banked by a '94' class tank. *Derek Cross*

Left: In 1955, tests were made on the Lickey Incline to assess the ability of 'Jubilees' and Class 5s to work passenger trains without assistance in rear. Here No 45554 *Ontario* with eight coaches, which had been stopped near mp 55, struggles to restart her train and fails. *W. A. Camwell*

Below left: By contrast, Class 5 No 44776, with seven coaches and starting from Bromsgrove station, managed to reach the summit at Blackwell in the tests. However, the unbanked permitted load of 90 tons was not changed. *W. A. Camwell*

Above: Taking the route via Worcester, the 10.28 from Sheffield, with 'Jubilee' No 45675 *Hardy*, passes Droitwich Junction in April 1963. *A. A. Vickers*

Right: No 45685 *Barfleur* has 10 coaches behind her as she blasts up the 1 in 90 through Fishponds in almost full forward gear on a 1950 Up express. *Real Photos 1079*

Far right, top: No 45682 *Trafalgar*, on the 10.13 Bristol–Newcastle in 1953, passes her home base, Barrow Road shed, Bristol, working hard to rush the taxing bank to Fishponds. *D. T. Flook*

Somerset & Dorset

The S&D has had so much coverage elsewhere that more pictures seem superfluous. However, this one illustrates one of the line's curiosities, the reversal into or out of Templecombe Joint station. Class 5 No 45440, an old S&D stalwart, draws a

Bristol-Bournemouth passenger train round the sharp curve from Templecombe No 2 Junction on the S&D main line in November 1956. *C. P. Boocock*

To Manchester through the Peak

Above: No 44851 still seems in fair condition, though grimy, in July 1966 as she fights her way up the 1 in 91 to Chinley North Junction with a Saturday 10-coach train from Manchester Piccadilly to Yarmouth Vauxhall. *John Clarke*

Below: Two boys at Manchester Central seem quite blasé about steam as 'Jubilee' No 45652 *Hawke* pulls out at the head of a St Pancras express. She was a Trafford Park engine. *K. Field*

Takeover of the Great Central

Below: Where, 10 years earlier, the passenger workings had been hauled by 'A3s', 'V2s' and 'B1s', and less than a month before through running between Nottingham and Marylebone ceased, Class 5 No 45267 pauses at Brackley on an Up semi-fast. *J. Scrace*

Bottom: In the vast Nottingham Victoria station, which by 1964 had become much under used, rebuilt 'Jubilee' No 45735 *Comet* starts the Saturday 15.41 Skegness-Leicester, while a '9F' waits to take over a following Saturday holiday service. *J. S. Hancock*

Central Division

Below: In this 1948 picture, Wakefield Class 5 No 45225 has just shut off steam passing Luddendenfoot ready for the Sowerby Bridge stop, on a Liverpool Exchange-Newcastle express. *Real Photos 24194*

Bottom: Just into ex-Midland territory, as the signals confirm, No 44692 pulls away from Colne on a stopping train to Skipton in 1956. *C. P. Boocock*

Above: The general rundown of freight traffic is evident in this 1968 view of once-busy Rose Grove Yard, with No 45073 sizzling on a permanent way train while a Class 8F pulls out on a short coal train. *M. Dunnett*

Left: Class 5 No 45388 sets back her freight train, almost totally ignored by local residents, in a picture that sums up the Central Division scene. *Ian Krause*

The Beattock Route

Above: Things are busy at Beattock station in June 1964 with two Down freight trains waiting their turn as No 45236 makes her run at the bank with a Crewe-Perth train. *Derek Cross*

Right: Coming up to Greskine siding, half way up Beattock bank, 'Jubilee' No 45742 *Connaught*, now with single chimney again, has a comparatively easy task with a four-coach Carlisle-Glasgow stopping train in 1964. *Derek Cross*

Below right: The sight of a 'Jubilee' working well-nigh all out on Beattock is not easily forgotten. Here No 45738 *Samson* emulates her biblical namesake with a formidable 14-coach overnight Anglo-Scottish express, including two sleeping cars — about 450 tons — near Harthope in August 1963, with rear end assistance from a 2-6-4 tank. *W. J. V. Anderson*

Bottom right: Within a mile of Beattock Summit, the exhaust beat of No 45692 *Cyclops* echoes from the Harthope hills as she lifts a through freight for Mossend. *Derek Cross*

Left: St Rollox works seemed to take a delight in fitting Class 5s, originally built with boilers having the forward topfeed position, with those with topfeed just in front of the dome, and vice versa. No 44786 carries such a boiler in June 1964, and what is left of the topfeed casing is staying there by prayer alone. She is working an Up freight passing Elvanfoot. *Derek Cross*

Centre left: 'Jubilee' No 45653 *Barham* leans to the curve as she crosses the infant River Clyde at Lamington with a Blackpool-Glasgow express in July 1962. *Derek Cross*

Below left: The intermediate signalbox at Craigenhill, also guarding a level crossing south of Carluke, rattles as No 44702, also fitted with an incorrect type boiler, passes with a Down freight. *Derek Cross*

113

The Nithsdale Route to Glasgow

Above: Humble duty for Class 5 No 45192 as she heads north from Dumfries with empty ballast hoppers in 1963. The Lockerbie branch goes off on the left, and the Stranraer line comes in behind the engine. *Derek Cross*

Right: Coasting as she leans to the Ardoch curves in the Drumlanrig Gorge, No 44726 has no less than eight coaches on a Glasgow-Carlisle stopping train in July 1964. *Derek Cross*

Below right: No 45364 makes a spirited restart from New Cumnock while working a 1962 Dumfries-Glasgow football excursion. She has gained a more modern boiler with topfeed on the front ring, and a later 4,000gal tender with external sieve boxes. *Derek Cross*

Bottom right: An 11-coach Leicester-Glasgow excursion comes up to Polquhap summit in April 1962 behind rebuilt 'Jubilee' No 45736 *Phoenix*. *Derek Cross*

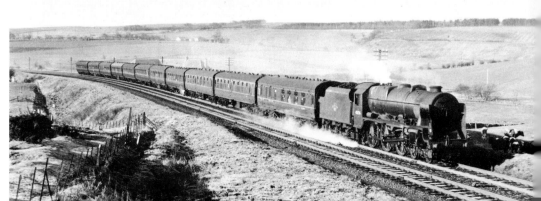

Highways and Byways of the Sou'West

Above: Travel *could* be a bit spartan when you travelled from Stranraer to St Enoch, 101 miles, in non-corridor stock! 'Jubilee' No 45621 *Northern Rhodesia* hurries a relief boat train away from Girvan in April 1961. One wonders what depot prank on the crew led to that 'L' on the smokebox door. *Derek Cross*

Centre left: With Kingmoor shed the possessor of Stephenson valve gear Class 5 No 44767 in 1966, it was inevitable that she would find her way on to the Stranraer line from time to time. Here she assists No 45168 to drag a Stranraer–Falkland Junction (Ayr) express freight off the Harbour branch at Girvan No 1 box. *Derek Cross*

Bottom left: Class 5s did a vast amount of hard work around the Ayrshire coalfield. Here No 44977 is passing Annbank, under clear signals just visible through the smoke, with mineral empties from Ayr bound for Killoch colliery. *Derek Cross*

Above right: No 45460, fitted with later type boiler, is making staccato music as she comes up to Tarbolton with a military vehicle special from Ayr in June 1963, headed for Mauchline and the G&SW line en route for Catterick.
Derek Cross

Right: Class 5 No 45474 has only six months to live as she battles her steamy way up gradients of 1 in 70 and 1 in 90 through Dailly with coal from Bargany colliery to Ayr Harbour (1966). *Derek Cross*

Below: Two Class 5s are needed to work this 10-coach Girvan-Greenock (Princes Pier) schools special up the 1 in 100 gradients past Kilmacolm in May 1964. They are Nos 45479 (tender first) and 44992. *Derek Cross*

Northwards from Buchanan Street

Above left: The 'St Mungo' from Aberdeen passes Stirling shed, a nine-coach train headed by 'Jubilee' No 45727 *Inflexible*.
Eric Treacy/P. B. Whitehouse collection

Left: Class 5 No 44994 at grips with Kinbuck bank, working a light-weight Edinburgh-Stirling-Perth service in 1963. *Derek Cross*

Below: An unidentified Class 5 is super-power for the two-coach Crieff branch train, here seen pulling out of Gleneagles. *G. H. Marsh*

Right: No 44997 has 12 coaches to lift up the mainly 1 in 121 and 1 in 100 bank to Gleneagles with an afternoon Up express, seen above Forteviot in September 1957. The first vehicle was the well-known Edinburgh District Engineer's saloon.
W. J. V. Anderson

Below right: The roof of Hilton Junction box, south of Perth, just shows above the leading vans of the 14.15 Aberdeen-Manchester fish train, emerging from the gloomy cutting from Moncrieff Tunnel behind No 45716 *Swiftsure* in March 1962.   *W. J. V. Anderson*

Bottom right: Beyond Moncrieff Tunnel, No 44959 has a Down freight for Perth Yard in this 1963 view passing Friarton.   *G. H. Marsh*

The Highland lines

Above: One of the toughest workings on the Highland main line was the overnight 'Royal Highlander' to Euston. Here the 14-coach train pulls out of Inverness behind its usual power, two Class 5s, in this case Nos 44788 (with earlier type boiler) and 44961. In 22 miles, much of it at 1 in 60, they have to get this heavy formation from near sea level to 1,315ft at Slochd Crossing. *Brian Morrison*

Below: At the other end of Inverness station in June 1951, the 10.45 from Kyle of Lochalsh, behind No 45138, takes the Rose Street curve avoiding the station, before propelling into the south platforms. The fireman has the single-line tablet ready for the Rose Street signalman. The leading vehicle is an ex-LNWR restaurant car. *E. D. Bruton*

Above: Class 5s were latterly the universal engines of the Highland lines. Here No 44798 has charge of a modest Down freight at The Mound. *G. Fairlie*

Below: In the last weeks of steam working on the Kyle line in 1961, No 45117 leaves Achanalt on the morning train for Inverness, having picked up the restaurant car (leading vehicle) at the previous station, Achnasheen, from the westbound 10.30 Inverness-Kyle. *W. J. V. Anderson*

To the Western Isles

Above left: The morning Fort William-Glasgow train is high above Loch Long, fighting up the 1 in 57 from Arrochar to Glen Douglas box in early 1959. Class 5 No 44957, one of a number which worked on the West Highland, is adding her muscle to that of unnamed Class K2/2 No 61786. *W. J. V. Anderson*

Left: Two locomotives for two coaches! The 15.57 from Ballachulish drifts down the 1 in 50 from Glencruitten Crossing into Oban in May 1960, with Class 5 No 44960 'assisting' ex-CR 0-4-4T No 55238. *M. Mensing*

Below: One of the four named Class 5s No 45157 *The Glasgow Highlander*, on the evening Glasgow-Oban train in June 1958, crossing the River Teith bridge in the Pass of Leny, just north of Callander. The first vehicle behind the tender is an ex-Pullman restaurant car. *W. J. V. Anderson*

On the Southern Region

Above: No 44870 has an 11-coach Bedford-Margate excursion in tow as she passes Bromley South in June 1959. *Derek Cross*

Right: A Nuneaton-Brighton excursion emerges from Quarry Tunnel in 1960 behind No 45147. *Derek Cross*

Below right: The 08.55 Bournemouth Central-Waterloo has strayed from its normal route, due to engineering works, and is sampling the Alton route with its single line at Itchen Abbas. The engine is No 45493, and the year 1966. *J. Scrace*

Royal Occasions

Below: A classic combination of two Class 5s for a Royal — Nos 45425 and 45454 approach Bare Lane bound for Morecambe in April 1955. Note the four-headlamp Royal Train headcode.
Ian Pearsall

Bottom: With a lesser formation than a full 'Royal', a single Class 5, No 44885 suffices to bring it over the old Dundee & Newtyle route from Alyth Junction. Here the train comes off the single line on to the Perth-Dundee main line at Ninewells Junction in June 1949. This appears to be an intermediate empty working in the programme.   *G. L. Wilson*

Above: Another Scottish event sees an Edinburgh-Glasgow Royal passing Shawfield in July 1958 behind Nos 45023 and 45024. *J. L. Stevenson*

Below: Royal Train worked tender-first? No, this is an empty stock working in the programme, returning from Ripon in May 1967, and seen here near Nidd Bridge. The engine is 'Jubilee' No 45562 *Alberta*. *G. W. Morrison*

7
Might-have-beens

There seems to have been no doubt at any time from Stanier's arrival in 1932 that one of his standard types would be a three-cylinder 4-6-0, based on the 'Patriot' concept, but with Stanier features exemplified by the tapered boiler. It was not until 1937, when thoughts turned to the use of a bigger boiler (which matured five years later as the '2A' boiler on Nos 5735 and 5736) that suggestions were made that two cylinders only would bring certain advantages, including a minimal increase in weight over the three-cylinder engine with '3A' boiler — and also some disadvantages. The proposal was not taken beyond the diagram stage in this form, for it became apparent that the three cylinders could be retained without the weight increase incurring an unacceptable penalty in route availability. I have traced no copy of the diagram for this two-cylinder 'Jubilee', but it apparently involved new wheels and motion to suit cylinders $19\frac{1}{4}$in × 28in[70] giving a tractive effort of 27,220lb. It is not clear why this approach was considered, when by retaining a 26in stroke, cylinders of $19\frac{5}{8}$in diameter would have been needed to maintain the existing tractive effort of 26,610lb. This might well have offered scope for a minor adaptation of the excellent cylinders used on the taper boiler 2-6-4 tank engines, though new motion would still have been required.

When it comes to the Class 5s, the early concept was not quite so clear cut. The Beames scheme for a modernised 'Prince of Wales' with Caprotti valve gear[71] found no sympathetic response from Stanier, and was immediately consigned to the waste paper basket in favour of an outside cylinder 4-6-0. An early Euston outline diagram (reproduced as Fig 19) shows that the main dimensions were laid down and remained unchanged, save for one important element, the boiler barrel diameter, shown as 5ft 6in only at the firebox end. This would have reduced the number of small tubes by something like 10, and probably when the first tubeplate layouts were being schemed out the advantages of the extra

$2\frac{1}{2}$in which were adopted were pointed out. Otherwise, and excepting the use of the 3,500gal Fowler tender, the differences were cosmetic — the lower footframing with small splashers, and the stovepipe chimney.

But an alternative version, probably slightly earlier in view of the safety valve 'bonnet' on the topfeed, has been illustrated by E. S. Cox,[72] and was a three-cylinder engine with $15\frac{1}{2}$in diameter cylinders; otherwise it followed the lines of the two-cylinder engine. It could have been expected to weigh about three tons more overall, and may well have met its downfall on this score, although maintenance costs would have been higher also.

There was, too, an abortive proposal for a light (Class 4) 4-6-0 for the Callander and Oban line, and for other Scottish routes requiring a lighter axleload.

As we have seen previously, as heavier coaching stock and higher average speeds were introduced over the years, the 'Jubilees' became somewhat outclassed and steadily more ill-matched to operating conditions and requirements. So the author remains convinced that for these engines to have made their proper contribution as a numerous second-line passenger class under the difficult and in some ways deteriorating conditions of the 1950s, it would have been necessary to make a more radical rebuild than was done in fitting 'Patriots' with the '2A' boiler, to give a larger grate area and thus the ability to burn inferior coal at lower combustion rates. The means existed in the new 'BR1' boiler used on the 'Britannias', and much of the existing chassis, wheels, bogie, outside cylinders, motion, etc, could have been re-used. The resulting rebuild, illustrated in the author's previous book,[73] would have raised the 'Jubilees' to a much-needed Class 7P. Regrettably, the need was not clearly foreseen in time, and with BR standard engines appearing in some quantity it was not a propitious time to be looking to major rebuilds of regional locomotive types. And yet... the Southern managed it!

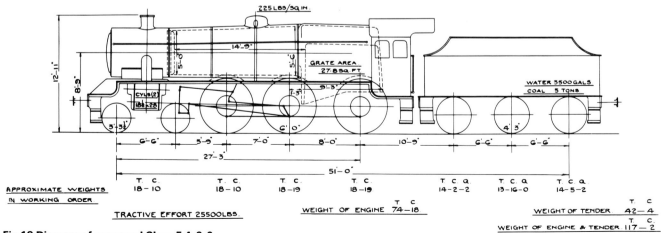

Fig 19 Diagram of proposed Class 5 4-6-0.
Crown Copyright National Railway Museum, York

8

Accidents

A comprehensive account of the accidents and major mishaps suffered by the 'Jubilees' and Class 5s could fill a book in itself; this is not altogether surprising for a group of 1,033 engines working in front-line service. Because they handled an appreciable amount of unfitted freight traffic — that bane of British railway operators — the Class 5s in particular were involved in numerous instances of 'running out of rail' in goods loops and elsewhere, ending up either in the ballast or down the bank. Virtually every case originated from some form of human error or misjudgement, either on the part of enginemen themselves, or of signalmen, permanent way staff and others. In no case was the design of these engines called into question at a Ministry inquiry, either as a direct or contributory cause, though there were one or two cases where standards of maintenance contributed to derailments on defective track. So there is a need to be selective in illustrating the main groups of incidents.

Several accidents occurred because the engine and train just happened to be in the wrong place at an unfortunate time. The supreme example was Harrow & Wealdstone on 8 October 1952, when the 08.00 Euston-Liverpool and Manchester express, double-headed by 'Jubilee' No 45637 and newly-rebuilt Pacific No 46202, ploughed into the wreckage of the rear-end collision between an Up express and a local passenger train. Both engines of the Liverpool train were so badly damaged that they were condemned on the spot. Another spectacular pileup took place north of Aviemore on 5 March 1940, when a Class 5 piloted by an ex-HR 'Loch' 4-4-0 working a Perth-Inverness freight were hit at very high speed by 21 wagons of coal and brake van, the rear portion of a preceding train which had run away down nine miles of steep gradients after a coupling snapped as it pulled into the loop at Slochd. Other examples were at Ardler Junction on 17 July 1948, in the Pass of Brander on 8 August 1946, between Garston and Hunts Cross on 24 November 1955, at Slade Lane Junction on 23 November 1959 and at Standon Bridge on 5 April 1960. Of wartime damage, there was also No 5425, badly damaged by a bomb at Crewe early in 1940

The passing of signals at danger always has a strong potential for trouble, and one such case provided the first instance of a Ministry inquiry involving a Stanier 4-6-0. This occurred at Rugby No 7 on 6 April 1936, when the 19.45 FF1 Camden-Edge Hill, hauled by 'Jubilee' No 5602, overran a signal despite repeated warning indications and side-swiped another express freight pulling out of the yard. Less than two years later, at Oakley Junction (north of Bedford) on 28 January 1938, the 14.10 St Pancras-Bradford, headed by 'Jubilee' No 5568, passed a signal at danger, was diverted on to the old Northampton branch and collided at about 25mph with 2-6-0 No 2893 which was

shunting empty stock. The front ends of the two engines were crumpled back until the smokeboxes touched. Another major pileup occurred in Bletchley station on 16 October 1939, when the 19.50 Euston-Stranraer (No 5025 piloting a 'Royal Scot') ran through signals while slowing for the station stop and hit at considerable speed an ex-LNW 0-8-0 which was detaching a van from a preceding train. Considerable damage to the station also resulted. In postwar years, with the spread of multiple aspect signalling, such cases became much rarer, but there was a case with marked similarities involving a Class 5 at Luton on 22 December 1955. On 20 July 1959 'Jubilee' No 45730 even managed to demolish Dock Junction signalbox, near St Pancras.

Excessive speed on curves led to two major accidents with Class 5s, both during 1955. On 23 January, engine No 45274, hauling the 12.15 York-Bristol (diverted from the normal Tamworth route by Sunday engineering work) failed to negotiate a 15-chain curve through Sutton Coldfield station, limited to 30mph, from a speed of at least 57. The engine and several coaches overturned. Then on 28 May No 45458, running tender first on a Tayport-Dundee excursion, overturned on the eight-chain curve in Wormit station, at the south end of the Tay Bridge, having run at 50-55mph into an area limited first to 20mph and finally to 10. Another instance of excessive speed, compounded by a signalman's error in prematurely clearing a home signal, led to a major collision on 9 June 1953; the 17.45 Keith-Inverness unfitted freight (No 44783 on 39 wagons and brake) had been running at mile-a-minute speeds, but was required to cross a passenger train from Inverness at Gollanfield Jucntion. As the passenger train approached the loop it was struck head-on by the freight at about 45mph, and its engine, ex-CR 4-4-0 No 54481, was damaged beyond repair.

Defective track, largely a postwar phenomenon, brought several engines to grief. At Wath Road Junction on 18 May 1948, 'Jubilees' Nos 5605 and 5608 double-heading the 11.45 St Pancras-Bradford encountered heat-buckled track at 60-65mph. In this subsidence area the track was ash-ballasted and was unstable. No 5605 was not derailed but No 5608 overturned. In two cases, on 16 August 1953 near Wilnecote involving 'Jubilee' No 45699 and on 22 November 1956 involving a Class 5, derailments occurred on unsatisfactory track to which the condition of engine and tender springs and/or weight adjustment were held to be contributory factors. There were also two cases, little more than 15 miles apart, when Class 5s ran on to track under repair at grossly excessive speed and were derailed (near Sandbach, 8 February 1960, and at Cheadle Hulme on 28 May 1964).

By far the greater number of accidents arose from signalmen's errors in semaphore signalled areas. Fortunately the results were seldom of great magnitude. Collisions occurred at Dale Lane, Kirkby, on 19 April 1945 involving Class 5 No 5210, and at Luddendenfoot on 21 February 1955 involving a 'Jubilee', when passenger trains struck engines and/or wagons standing unprotected on the main line, and there were further collisions at Preston station on 16 January 1958 (engine standing foul of a route set for a Class 5 hauled passenger train) and Ince Moss Junction on 17 February 1958. There were at least two collisions between Class 5s and road vehicles on manned level crossings in Scotland.

Occasional mishaps resulted from defective signalling equipment. One such case occurred at Dumfries on 12 June 1944, when 'Jubilee' No 5660 on an empty stock train hit a standing push/pull train. Perhaps the worst occurred at Lichfield on 1 January 1946, when the very light 14.50 Fleetwood-Broad St fish train, hauled by No 5495, was diverted into the Up platform at about 35mph after the loop points had failed to return to normal due to obstruction and buckled point rodding, and hit a standing local train. At Alloa Junction on 10 January 1951, under block failure conditions following heavy snow, the 07.00 Perth-Buchanan St, hauled by No 44786, ran at excessive speed during Time Interval working and hit light engine No 45482 standing on the main line. Another instance, compounded by signalman's error, occurred at Chinley on 8 March 1958, when a 'Jubilee'-worked football excursion returning from Luton was wrongly signalled into an occupied platform while track circuit failures were causing problems.

Yet in spite of all these knocks, engines were put back into traffic with straightened frames and other major surgery, and it is a tribute to the general robustness of the Stanier 4-6-0s that until the mid-1960s, when steam was being run down, the only premature withdrawal was of the battered No 45637 in 1952 after her ordeal at Harrow.

Appendices

1 Frame Fractures

Statistically the first 452 Class 5s were regarded as 'bad' for frame fracturing, but were surpassed by certain other classes. The position up to June 1943 for selected classes was:

Class	Built	No in service	Cracks/ engine/ 10 years	General impression	Remarks
6P 'Royal Scot'	1927-30	71	14.5	Very bad	Cracks at all horn gaps
5MT 4-6-0	1934-37	452	3.0*	Bad	See below
4MT 2-6-4T pb	1927-34	125	2.7	Poor	Most cracks at Driving horn gaps
8F 2-8-0	1935 on	Over 200	1.7	Poor	Most cracks at Driving horn gaps
5XP 4-6-0 tb.	1934-37	191	1.2	Fair	Most cracks at Trailing horn gaps
5XP 4-6-0 pb.	1930-34	52	0.5	Good	
7P 4-6-2 'Princess'	1933-35	13	0.4	Good	Cracking most prevalent behind outside cylinders

*Average incidence for Nos 5000-5224 was 4.0, for Nos 5225-5451 was 2.0.

Cracking at horn gaps was almost invariably in one of six places, three in front of, and three behind, the gap. These were:

— from the radius of the top corners,
— from the top rivet hole for the axlebox guide,
— from the corner of the bottom notch for the horn stay.

The record for 134 Crewe-maintained Class 5s between Nos 5000 and 5224 showed that the LH frame was rather more prone to cracking than the RH one, and the totals from new up to June 1943 were:

While cracking could start after as little as two years, there was usually freedom for five years, after which it continued at an accelerating pace. There were modest differences in the pattern between different batches, due to design changes. First cracks were usually at the horn stay notches.

In some cases, cracks from the top back corner of the leading horn gap had extended almost to the top of the frame. The large number of cracks from the top back corner of the driving horn gap was thought to be due to an access hole for the front firebox washout plugs. The retrospective fitting of cross-stays to the leading axlebox guides, as on the trailing axlebox guides from new, appeared to be leading to an increase in top corner cracks, for no apparent reason. There was some evidence that Class 5s of the Nos 5000-5224 group working in Scotland were more prone to cracking than the English-allocated ones, and further analysis led inexorably to the conclusion that the main factor was high piston thrusts, together with flexing of the frame due to the $4\frac{3}{8}$in offset of the centreline of the axlebox guides from the frame. This was evidenced by the serious wear and fretting corrosion of the horn stay mating surfaces, up to .060in at the inside and up to .030in adjacent to the frame. Workshop practice, in the finishing of the top corner radii and horn stay notches to avoid stress-raisers, and to a lesser extent in the fitting of the horn stays, were contributing factors.

Tests made in the Derby station area with No 5088 having the area above the leading horngap strain-gauged, confirmed the predominant effect of piston thrust; when working heavily the range of stress was 12-16tons/sq in, with a recorded maximum of 17.9ton/sq in. To give more precise information, a full-size section of Class 5 frame at the leading horn gap, complete with axlebox guides, horn stays, etc, was manufactured, loaded in a special Research Department rig for cylinder cover load (40 tons) across the gap, and both frame plate and horn stay strain-gauged at various degrees of

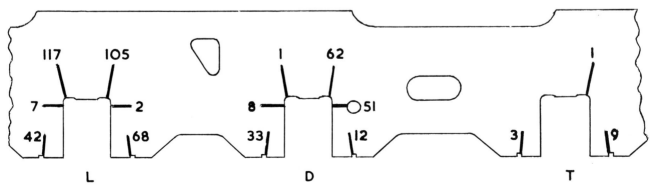

Fig 20 Pattern of frame fractures, Class 5 4-6-0.

tightness of the horn stay nuts. Some of the figures obtained were:

Stay	Stay Nuts	Av stress in plate at top corners tons/sq in	Load carried by stay ton
Tight	Tight	5.5	13.2
.020in slack	Tight	12.5	9.4
.035in slack	Just nipped	17.0	1.9
Removed	—	over 18	—

Further work simulated the off-set loading of the frame through the axlebox guide. The whole series of tests showed 'the overwhelming importance of a tight connection at the bottom of the horn gap' and that 'certain forms of horn stay are inherently impossible to keep tight in consequence of fretting corrosion'. An increase in frame stress due to off-set loading was established, 'not only in its direct effect on the frame itself but also indirectly in setting up fretting of the horn stay joint surfaces'.

This work, allied to the first-class record in frame durability of the Horwich 2-6-0 engines of 1926, led to the adoption on all subsequent new Class 5s (and other classes) of the Horwich-type horn stay bolted directly to extended legs of the frame plate itself, of one-piece hornblocks on Leading and Driving horn gaps, and of pin-jointed cross-stays at all horn gap positions.

At this time (early 1940s) the standard repair practice for cracked frames involved 'veeing' out the crack and rewelding. This was not successful, and usually led to recracking at the edge of the weld. In most cases a horse-shoe patch was riveted to the outside of the frame plate at the driving axle horngap, but this effected little real strengthening of the frames. A technique was therefore developed of cutting out cracked material and welding in large inserts of new plate in lieu. Four basic types of insert were evolved, permitting vertical or near-vertical welds kept well away from highly

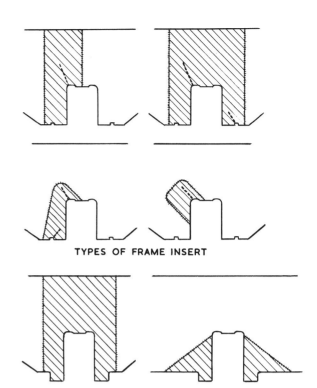

TYPES OF FRAME INSERT

CLASS 5   JUBILEE
FITTING OF HORWICH HORNCLIPS

Fig 21 Frame repairs by welding in inserts.

stressed areas, some of which could be fitted with the boiler in position. Even these inserts changed somewhat over the years, and the surgery carried out on the 'Jubilee' frames when fitted with manganese steel liners and Horwich horn stays was probably unique in welding in no less than *six* triangular inserts in *each* frame plate (Fig 21).

2 Class 6P 4-6-0 'Jubilees': Valve Events

Walschaerts valve gear, inside admission
Steam lap: $1\frac{7}{16}$in*
Lead: $\frac{1}{4}$in*
Exhaust clearance: Nil
Port width: $1\frac{3}{4}$in

Nominal Cutoff %	Valve Travel in	Lead in F B	Port Opening in F B	Cutoff % F B	Release % F B	Compression % F B
Outside Motion						
45	4.08	.25 .25	.58 .62	45 44	80.5 78.6	78.6 80.5
30	3.71	.25 .25	.41 .42	30 31	73.3 72.3	72.3 73.3
20	3.52	.25 .25	.32 .32	20 20.4	66.4 65.2	65.2 66.4
15	3.44	.25 .25	.28 .28	15 14.6	61.0 60.5	60.5 61.0
Inside Motion						
45	4.13	.25 .25	.56 .69	45 45.3	81.0 78.5	78.5 81.0
30	3.71	.25 .25	.39 .44	30 31	74.0 71.8	71.8 74.0
20	3.51	.25 .25	.30 .33	20 20.2	66.5 65.2	65.2 66.5
15	3.44	.25 .25	.28 .28	15 14.5	60.0 60.0	60.0 60.0

Drawings D34-13593
        D34-13594

* Steam lap and lead subsequently altered to $1\frac{3}{8}$in and $\frac{5}{16}$in respectively, but events never revised from valve gear model

3 Class 5MT 4-6-0 Locomotives: Valve Events

Walschaerts Valve Gear, inside admission.
Steam lap: $1\frac{1}{2}$in
Lead: $\frac{1}{4}$in (nominal)
Exhaust clearance $\frac{1}{16}$in
Port width: 2in (originally $1\frac{3}{4}$in)

Drawing C33605

Nominal Cutoff %	Valve Travel in	Lead in		Port Opening				Area of port Opening sq in				Cutoff %		Release %		Compression %	
				Inlet		Exhaust		Inlet		Exhaust							
		F	B	F	B	F	B	F	B	F	B	F	B	F	B	F	B
50	4.567	.273	.227	.750	.797	2.0	2.0	17.87	18.75	48.70	47.90	50.2	49.5	82.0	79.2	81.2	84.0
40	4.187	.273	.227	.594	.594	2.0	2.0	14.0	13.80	48.70	47.90	40.5	40.5	77.5	75.0	77.2	79.7
30	3.906	.273	.227	.453	.453	2.0	2.0	10.75	10.65	48.70	47.90	30.5	30.5	72.0	70.0	72.5	74.7
20	3.687	.273	.227	.331	.336	1.891	1.906	8.30	8.10	46.15	45.85	20.2	20.2	64.5	63.0	66.0	67.7

Caprotti Poppet Valve Gear (Nos 44738-44757).
Engines as built.

Nominal Cutoff %	Lead in	Valve Opening in		Area of Port Opening sq in		Cutoff %	Release %	Compression %
		Inlet	Exhaust	Inlet	Exhaust			
50	.250	.797	1.078	27.54	32.60	50	85.5	40.5
40	.297	.797	1.078	27.54	32.60	40	85.5	40.5
30	.312	.797	1.078	27.54	32.60	30	85.5	40.5
20	.312	.672	1.078	24.80	32.60	20	85.5	40.5
10	.312	.484	1.078	18.60	32.60	10	85.5	40.5

Drawing DD3865

4 Wheel Balancing

Hammerblow Particulars

Class	Recip Wt per Cylinder, lb		% Balance		Speed		Hammerblow, tons			
	I	O	I	O	rps	mph	Per Wheel	Per Axle	Per Rail	Whole eng
5X	751	750	66.6	66.6	5	71	3.06	0.23	8.31	0.61
					8	115	7.84	0.59	21.20	1.56
5	—	933	—	66.6	5	64	3.84	4.28	10.36	11.52
				50	5	64	2.95	3.50	7.59	9.03
				30	5	64	1.76	2.10	4.04	4.83
				66.6	8	103	9.82	11.00	26.60	29.55
				50	8	103	7.41	8.78	19.03	22.66
				30	8	103	4.51	5.38	10.34	12.36

In two-cylinder engines the reciprocating balance was divided equally between the coupled wheels, to minimise the blow per wheel and per axle. The 'Jubilees' had the reciprocating balance for both inside and outside cylinders similarly divided; there was thus in each wheel a component for the inside cylinder, outside cylinder on that side, and cross-couple effect of the opposite outside cylinder. The resultant hammerblow is in nearly opposite directions in the LH and RH wheels, so that while there is a very appreciable blow in each wheel and each rail, there is only a negligible blow in each axle and for the engine as a whole.[74]

High-speed Tests with Class 5s on greased rail, 1939

The engines used were: No 5043 with 66.6% reciprocating balance, No 5464 with 50% reciprocating balance and No 5406 specially altered to give 30% reciprocating balance.

These were run on to greased track at 10-18mph with regulator wide open. The results were:

Engine	5043	5464	5406
% Recip Balance	66.6	50	30
Slip speed, mph	103	104	99
Max lift of driving wheel from rail	2.4in	0.4in	None
Fore-and-aft oscillation	Nothing abnormal	Moderate	Excessive

With No 5043 the hammerblow per wheel in its upwards phase exceeded the static wheel load of 8.95 tons, allowing wheel lift; while this was not theoretically the case with No 5464, the dynamics of the wheel/rail system were such as to induce lift. In the case of No 5043 this lift was much greater than the flange depth; with this engine in particular this resulted in severe damage to the track, with rails badly bent and the ballast damaged to give permanent settlement.

5 Weight Adjustment with Cottered Spring Links

Class 5 4-6-0 No 44716   Crewe Works, 18 June 1953.

1 Diagram weights (tons).

	Bogie	Coupled			Total
		L	D	T	
	18.1	18.55	18.75	18.1	73.5

2 Actual weights as received from erecting shop. ($11\frac{3}{4}$in spring links and 2in cotters throughout).

		Bogie		Coupled			Total
		L	T	L	D	T	
	R	3.65	3.85	11.3	8.9	7.95	
	L	3.95	3.95	10.2	9.35	9.55	
Total		15.4		21.5	18.25	17.5	72.65
Axlebox Top Clearance	R	$1\frac{1}{8}$in	$2\frac{1}{16}$in	$1\frac{9}{16}$in	$1\frac{7}{8}$in	2in	
	L	$1\frac{1}{8}$in	$2\frac{1}{4}$in	$1\frac{11}{16}$in	$1\frac{3}{4}$in	$2\frac{1}{16}$in	

3 Weights after adjusting bogie spring links to take more weight on bogie (tons).

		Bogie		Coupled			Total
		L	T	L	D	T	
	R	4.2	4.1	10.1	9.55	7.75	
	L	4.2	3.9	9.45	9.65	9.95	
Total		16.4		19.55	19.2	17.7	72.85

4 Some cotters changed to even up coupled axle weights (Time: 35min)

		Bogie		Coupled			Total
		L	T	L	D	T	
Cotters	R	—	—	$1\frac{15}{16}$in	NC	$2\frac{1}{16}$in	
	L	—	—	NC	$1\frac{15}{16}$in	$1\frac{15}{16}$in	
Weights after alteration	R	4.25	4.15	9.4	9.5	8.5	
	L	4.3	4.1	9.45	9.4	9.55	
Total		16.8		18.85	18.9	18.05	72.6

5 Final cotter change to increase weight on RT wheel (Time: 8min)

		Bogie		Coupled			Total
		L	T	L	D	T	
Cotters	R	—	—	$1\frac{15}{16}$in	NC	$2\frac{1}{8}$in	
	L	—	—	NC	$1\frac{15}{16}$in	$1\frac{15}{16}$in	
Weights after alteration	R	4.15	4.15	9.85	9.1	8.9	
	L	4.25	4.05	9.75	9.3	9.4	
Total		16.6		19.6	18.4	18.3	72.9
Axlebox top Clearance	R	$1\frac{3}{8}$in	$2\frac{5}{16}$in	$1\frac{11}{16}$in	$1\frac{15}{16}$in	2in	
	L	$1\frac{1}{4}$in	$2\frac{5}{16}$in	$1\frac{11}{16}$in	$1\frac{11}{16}$in	$1\frac{7}{8}$in	

It will be seen that the bogie was sitting 'nose down' under the spherical bolsters, though this was not affecting the weight distribution within the bogie (see Chapter 2, item 7).

6 Class 5MT 4-6-0s — Valve Setting

Following complaints from the Motive Power Department in Scotland in 1947 about heavy trailing axlebox knock with new Horwich-built Class 5s with manganese steel axlebox liners, the cause was identified as faulty valve setting.[52] An assessment was made of the adjustments to be made when setting valves cold, in order to produce the designed events under working conditions, hot. The elements are:

1 Expansion of the frame plate and cylinder flange, forwards from the rear edge of the flange.
2 Expansion of the valve chest between the ports, about the centre-line.
3 Expansion of the valve spindle, forwards from the valve spindle crosshead.

Making realistic assumptions of temperatures, and based on these expansion patterns, it can be shown that when hot the front port lead will increase by about .045in and the back port lead will decrease by about .052in (see Fig 22).

The drawing leads were .273inF and .227inB, so that the corrected leads when cold should be approximately .228inF and .279inB. For practical purposes the works used figures of $^7/_{32}$inF and $^9/_{32}$inB, roughly equivalent to shimming both heads back $^1/_{16}$in from the design leads. In practice this led to excessive work at the rear end of the cylinder, while reversing the leads to $^9/_{32}$inF and $^7/_{32}$inB also reversed the balance of work done. It is reasonable to suppose that by setting the valve heads cold to $^1/_4$in lead at both ends, the work done would have been roughly equalised at each end of the cylinder.

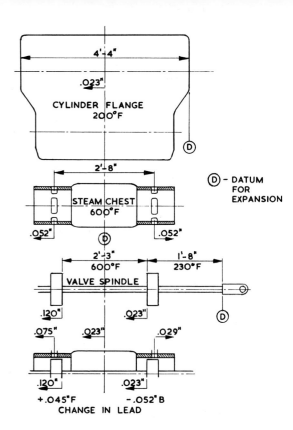

Fig 22 Thermal expansion effects on valve setting, Class 5 4-6-0.

7 Mileage, Availability and Utilisation

The utilisation of 'Jubilees' and Class 5s (as with many other classes) was more intensive in the later 1930s than was the case postwar. As an example, 'Jubilees' in Scotland were averaging 63,138 miles a year in 1937, whereas in postwar years they never bettered 51,936 miles, and even this was a 16% improvement on 1950/51 as a result of CME pressure on the Operating Department; the number of engine days stopped for shop or shed repairs had not increased.

The 'Individual Costing' scheme, restarted in 1950 after lapsing during World War 2, and continuing until 1957, showed 'Jubilees' averaging 200-230 miles per day, and Class 5s averaging 160 miles per day on the LM Region and 185 miles per day in Scotland, where they did a rather higher proportion of longer passenger work. The days per year under and awaiting repair over the period of the costing scheme averaged:

		Works*	Depots
'Jubilee'	LMR	27	50
	ScR†‡	27	47
Class 5	LMR	19	35
	ScR†‡	26	43

* Strictly, these figures apply to classified repairs only, but the difference is negligible.
† Average 1953-57 inclusive; works figures for 1950-52 were untypically high at St Rollox.
‡ Higher Class 5 figures partially reflect faster buildup of mileage producing shorter shopping and examination periods.

The difference in mileage, availability and utilisation for different batches of Class 5s within the 'Roller Bearing Experiment' should not be read as having any deep significance. Much depended on the depot to which allocated and the nature of the work performed there. No

instructions were issued to utilise the engines more intensively than other representatives of the class. Over the eight-year period (less for some batches built after 1949) the days per year under and awaiting repair, and mileage run — all on the LM Region except where indicated — averaged:

	Repair Days		Mileage
	Works	Depots	
Std Walschaerts, plain bearings	18	40	42,766
Std engines not in 'experiment'	19	35	39,704
Walschaerts, Timken bearings	23	33	43,848
Walschaerts, Skefco bearings	22	37	42,063
Walschaerts, Timken D only	15	38	47,609
Walschaerts, Skefco D only (ScR)	13	42	50,442
Stephenson, Timken bearings	27	49	53,251
Caprotti, plain bearings	29	37	41,213
Caprotti, Timken bearings	31	41	44,678
Caprotti, Skefco D only*	33	42	43,032

* For reasons not now apparent, the official annual statements from 1953 onwards show only one engine in this group, with one extra in the group of Caprotti, Timken bearing engines.

One would be hard driven to draw any very meaningful conclusions from these figures, which (particularly at depots) could be 'laundered' without undue difficulty if desired. For instance, would the use of Skefco bearings on the driving axle only, with a total of 55 days per year under or awaiting repair and an annual mileage of over 50,000, necessarily improve by two days per year and over 8,000 miles over the same engine with Skefco bearings throughout, under comparable conditions? And No 44767, the Stephenson valve gear engine, with the highest annual mileage of any group *and* the highest number of days stopped for repair — what lesson does this teach, other than that the depot to which she was allocated managed to keep her on work more productive than average?

8 Draughting and Gas Flow Proportions — 'Jubilees'

Postwar work at Swindon on optimum blastpipe/chimney proportions demonstrated that the standard 'Jubilee' draughting was fairly close to the ideal, as the table below shows, but would probably have benefited from the chimney choke being lowered 3-4in relative to the blastpipe cap. The marginal superiority of the Class 5 draughting is evident.

	'Jubilee'		Class 5	
	Theory	*Actual*	*Theory*	*Actual*
Blastpipe dia (min)	4.94in	4.75in	4.95in	5.12in
Choke dia	14.32in	14.25in	14.35in	14.25in
Height — Blastpipe to choke	33.00in	36.37in	33.06in	33.62in
Height — choke to chimney top	26in min	25.5in	26in min	24.37in
Chimney taper	1 in 14	1 in 7	1 in 14	1 in 7

The deficiency in free gas area of the sloping throatplate 'Jubilee' boiler, brought about by the use of $1\frac{3}{8}$in dia superheater elements and shown up in the Rugby tests on No 45722, could have been largely overcome by the use of the Class 5 28-element tubeplates, as the following table shows; a reversion to $1\frac{1}{4}$in dia elements with these tubeplates would have brought an even greater improvement.

Line	Flues	Element dia	Small Tubes	Free Gas Area			S'heater as % of total	Gas Area as % of grate
				Sup	Small Tubes	Total		
15	24	$1\frac{1}{4}$in	159	2.16	2.34	4.50	48.0	14.5
New	28	$1\frac{1}{4}$in	151	2.52	2.22	4.74	53.2	15.3
17	24	$1\frac{3}{8}$in	159	1.99	2.34	4.33	46.0	14.0
New	28	$1\frac{3}{8}$in	151	2.32	2.22	4.54	51.1	14.6

9 Preserved Locomotives

Four 'Jubilees' and 14 Class 5s have been preserved, though at the time of writing (April 1983) not all have yet been restored to working order. They are:

'Jubilees'

5593*	*Kolhapur*		7029 Clun Castle Ltd, Tyseley.
5596*	*Bahamas*	Double chimney	Bahamas Locomotive Society, Dinting.
5690	*Leander*		Private, Carnforth.
45699	*Galatea*		Leander Locomotive Ltd, Carnforth.

Class 5's

4767†	*George Stephenson*	Stephenson valve gear & Timken bearings	At North Yorkshire Moors Railway, Grosmont.
44806†	*Magpie*		At Steamtown Transport Museum, Southport.
44871			At Carnforth.
44932			At Carnforth.
45000*			British Railways Board. On loan to Severn Valley Railway, Bridgnorth.
5025*			Private. At Strathspey Railway, Boat of Garten.
45110*†	*RAF Biggin Hill*		Stanier Black 5 Locomotive Preservation Society at Severn Valley Railway, Bridgnorth.
45212*			At Keighley & Worth Valley, Railway, Haworth.
5231†	*3rd (Volunteer) Battalion, The Worcestershire and Sherwood Foresters Regiment*		Great Central Railway, Loughborough.
45305			A. E. Draper, restored by Humberside Locomotive Preservation Group.
45379			Bristol Suburban Railway Society, Bitton.
5407			At Steamtown Transport Museum, Southport.
5428†	*Eric Treacy*		Stanier Black 5 Locomotive Preservation Society, on loan to North Yorkshire Moors Railway, Grosmont.
5491			West Lancs Black 5 Group, Blackpool.

† Named since withdrawal by BR.
* With straight throatplate boiler.

Above: Birds of a feather—
The Swindon origins of some
features of the 'Jubilee'
design — and at the same
time the major differences —
can be compared in this view
of No 5593 *Kolhapur* with
'Castle' class 4-6-0 No 7029
Clun Castle at Tyseley.
P. B. Whitehouse

Right: No 5690 *Leander* is
working under easy steam as
she crosses Arten Gill
Viaduct, just south of Dent,
on a special on 26 April 1980
made up of BR Mk 1 stock.
J. H. Cooper-Smith

Left: From Standedge Tunnel, just over three miles long, *Leander* emerges on a 'Trans Pennine Pullman' working on 10 April 1982 and begins the coasting descent towards Huddersfield. *J. H. Cooper-Smith*

Below left: On a special steam working to Hexham for the Stephenson 200 Carnival celebrating the great engineer's birth, No 4767 *George Stephenson* is passing Blaydon with 12 coaches in tow, on 6 June 1981.
J. H. Cooper-Smith

Below: Making her presence felt among the tower blocks and industrial wilderness of Manchester, Class 5 No 5000, after arrival from Liverpool, slips to a standstill on the vicious start from Victoria while taking the empty stock up to Red Bank sidings on 22 June 1980. *J. H. Cooper-Smith*

Above left: Another pair of kindred parentage. Class 5 No 5000 pilots 'Hall' No 4930 *Hagley Hall* on a 12-coach 'Welsh Marches Pullman' as they tackle the 1 in 80 up from Penpergwm to Nantyderry, on 20 March 1982. *J. H. Cooper-Smith*

Left: To the mountains . . . Northbound on a Perth–Aviemore special on 20 July 1981, No 5025 breasts the 1,484ft Druimuachdar Summit. *J. H. Cooper-Smith*

Above: And the Sea . . . No 5025 winds her Kyle-bound special along the shore of Loch Carron near Attadale on 29 May 1982. *J. H. Cooper-Smith*

Above right: On a crisp day in March 1980, with snow on the fells, No 5305, working very nearly in full gear, comes up to Ais Gill distant signal on the 'Cumbrian Mountain Express' from Carlisle. *J. H. Cooper-Smith*

Right: On 1 May 1982 on the 'Cumbrian Mountain Pullman', No 5407 is being worked hard on the 1 in 128 approaching Clapham. *J. H. Cooper-Smith*

Above: Two days later, looking slightly less pristine in appearance, No 5407 again heads the 'Cumbrian Mountain Pullman' at Giggleswick.
J. H. Cooper-Smith

Above right: On the North Yorkshire Moors Railway, Class 5 No 5428, apparently afflicted by a sticking RH cylinder cock, emerges from Grosmont Tunnel in a picture which typifies the lasting appeal of steam.
J. H. Cooper-Smith

Right: Finale. As evening comes, and the outline of the Cuillin Hills in Skye softens, Class 5 No 5025 gently heads back from Kyle of Lochalsh to Inverness, light engine because no turning facilities now exist at Kyle.
J. H. Cooper-Smith

10 Locomotive Drawings

The standard rebuilt 'Royal Scot' design.

These drawings are included for comparison purposes.

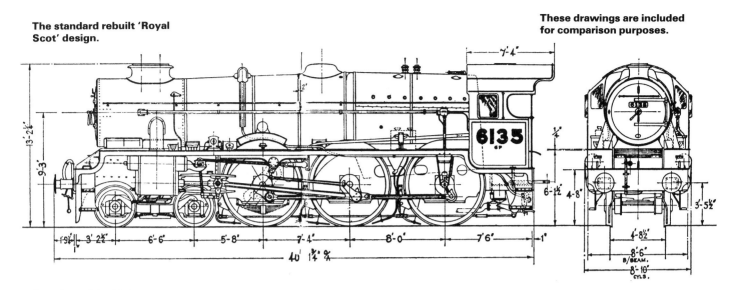

Drawing of the high pressure locomotive No 6399 *Fury*.

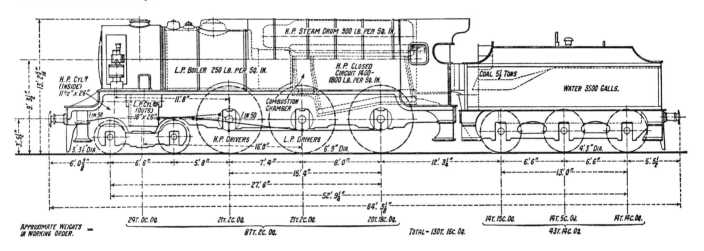

No 6399 *Fury* as rebuilt by Stanier to form the basic prototype of the rebuilt 'Royal Scots' it was renumbered 6170 *British Legion*.

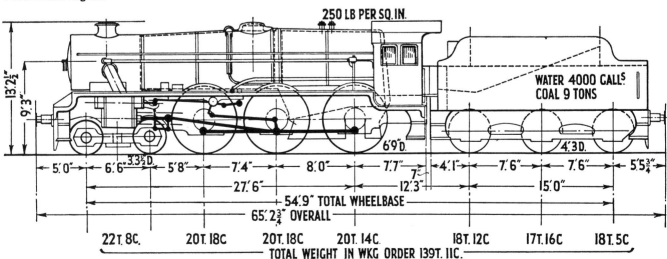

139

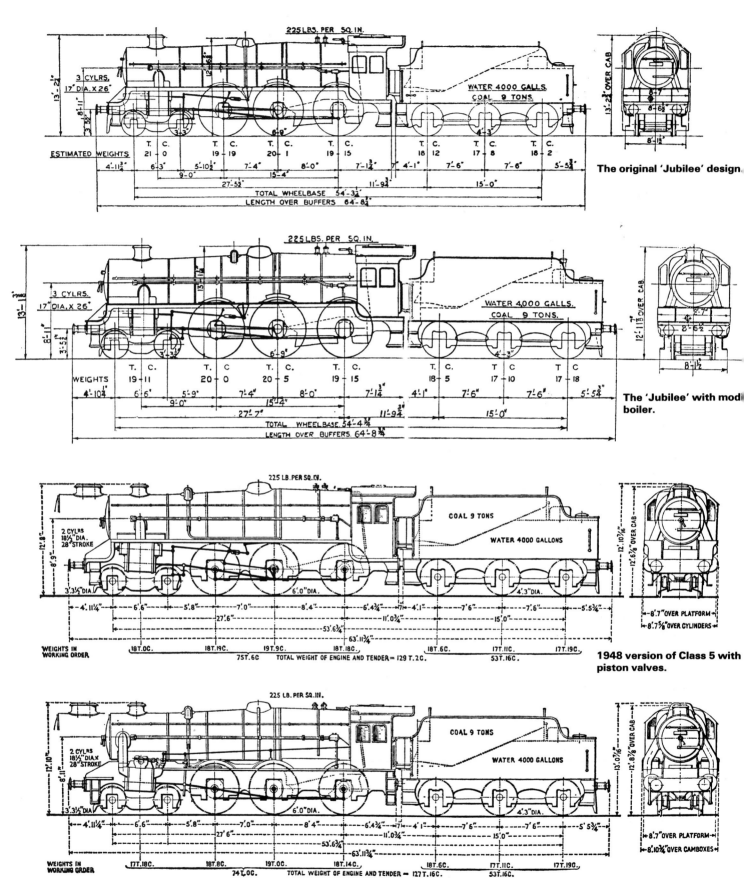

225 LBS. PER SQ. IN.

3 CYLRS.
17" DIA. X 26"

WATER 4000 GALLS.
COAL 9 TONS.

13'-2¼" OVER CAB

		T.	C.		T.	C.		T.	C.		T.	C.		T.	C.		T.	C.		T.	C.
ESTIMATED WEIGHTS		21	0		19	19		20	1		19	15		18	12		17	8		18	2

TOTAL WHEELBASE 54'-3¼"
LENGTH OVER BUFFERS 64'-8¼"

The original 'Jubilee' design.

225 LBS. PER SQ. IN.

3 CYLRS.
17" DIA. X 26"

WATER 4000 GALLS.
COAL 9 TONS.

12'-11⅝" OVER CAB

		T.	C.		T.	C.		T.	C.		T.	C.		T.	C.		T.	C.		T.	C.
WEIGHTS		19	11		20	0		20	5		19	15		18	5		17	10		17	18

TOTAL WHEELBASE 54'-4¾"
LENGTH OVER BUFFERS. 64'-8¾"

The 'Jubilee' with mod boiler.

225 LB. PER SQ. IN.

2 CYLRS
18½" DIA.
28" STROKE

COAL 9 TONS

WATER 4000 GALLONS

12'-10⅞" OVER CAB
12'-6⅞" OVER CAB

WEIGHTS IN WORKING ORDER

18T.0C.	18T.19C.	19T.9C.	18T.18C.	18T.6C.	17T.11C.	17T.19C.

75T.6C.   TOTAL WEIGHT OF ENGINE AND TENDER = 129 T.2C.   53T.16C.

8'.7" OVER PLATFORM
8'.7⅝" OVER CYLINDERS

1948 version of Class 5 with piston valves.

225 LB. PER SQ. IN.

2 CYLAS
18½" DIA X
28" STROKE

COAL 9 TONS

WATER 4000 GALLONS

13'.0⅞" OVER CAB
12'.8⅞" OVER CAB

WEIGHTS IN WORKING ORDER

17T.18C.	18T.8C.	19T.0C.	18T.14C.	18T.6C.	17T.11C.	17T.19C.

74T.0C.   TOTAL WEIGHT OF ENGINE AND TENDER = 127 T.16C.   53T.16C.

8'.7" OVER PLATFORM
8'.10¾" OVER CAMBOXES

Class 5 with Caprotti valve motion.

140

References

Chapter 1

1 *A Modern Locomotive History: Ten Years Development on the LMS, 1923-1932*, E. S. Cox, Proceedings of the Institution of Locomotive Engineers, Vol 190, 1946.
2 *Mendips Enginemen*, Peter Smith; Oxford Publishing Co, 1972.

Chapter 2

3 *Approach to Modernisation*, Presidential Address to the Institution of Locomotive Engineers, E. S. Cox; Proc Inst Loco E Vol 258, 1957.
4 *Living with London Midland Locomotives*, A. J. Powell; Ian Allan, 1977.
5 *The Stanier 4-6-0's of the LMS*, J. W. P. Rowledge and Brian Reed; David & Charles, 1977.
6 Rowledge & Reed quote this change as made from No 5225, but this is incorrect. The 227 Armstrong Whitworth engines Nos 5225-5451 had frames 1in thick of steel to LMS Spec 4B, a low-alloy weldable steel similar to the 'Chromador' steel used on Nos 5125-5224.
7 *The British Steam Railway Locomotive, 1925-65*, O. S. Nock; Ian Allan, 1966. Fig 136.
8 O. S. Nock, op cit (7), Fig 216.
9 Rowledge & Reed, op cit (5), Fig 17.
10 *Railway Gazette*, 5 June 1936.
11 *SLS Journal*, February 1979.
12 Rowledge & Reed, op cit (5) give the piston valve diameter as an 'unusual' $10\frac{5}{8}$in, but this is incorrect.
13 Rowledge & Reed, op cit (5) state that the mechanical lubricators were driven from the combination levers, but this was not so; such an arrangement would have given a variable delivery according to cutoff. In fact they were driven from small crank arms on the inner trunnions of the expansion links, the standard arrangement on all LMS engines with Walschaerts valve gear save for the taper boiler 2-6-0s Nos 2945-2984 and a few early Class 5s from Vulcan Foundry, where the outside trunnion was used.
14 O. S. Nock, op cit (7), Fig 214.
15 Rowledge & Reed, op cit (5).
16 A. J. Powell, op cit (4), Fig 1.
17 In the 1950s a fireman on the Western Region was fatally injured when doing this, the fireiron striking an overbridge.
18 An experiment was carried out in 1939 on No 5698 with a small ash disposal chute at the smokebox front, and during World War 2 a number of 'Jubilees' and Class 5s were fitted experimentally with an arrangement of water jets in the smokebox bottom to eject ash. These arrangements were abandoned in favour of self-cleaning smokeboxes on new construction.

19 The hard and unpleasant nature of this work is well captured by Terry Essery in his book *Firing Days at Saltley*, Chapter IV; Bradford Barton, 1980.

Chapter 3

20 *Some New Developments of the Stephenson Boiler*, R. P. Wagner. Proc Inst Loco E, Vol 93, 1929.
21 *A Study of the Locomotive Boiler*, Lawford H. Fry; Simmons-Boardman Publishing Co, 1924.
22 *Locomotive Boiler Design: Theory and Practice*, M. M. Loubser and E. S. Cox; Proc Inst Loco E, Vol 144, 1938.
23 E. S. Cox, Letter to the author.
24 *Railway Magazine*, November 1934.
25 The LMS used codes for its fitted freight trains. 'FF1' was a No 1 fitted freight, with all vehicles vacuum-fitted or piped, while 'FF2', the No 2 fitted freight, had to have a minimum of one third vehicles vacuum fitted or piped. There were limits to the proportion of piped-only vehicles.
26 *Locomotive Panorama*, Vol 1, E. S. Cox; Ian Allan, 1965.
27 G. J. Aston, *SLS Journal*, May 1979.
28 It has been suggested by Col H. C. B. Rogers in his book *Bulleid Pacifics at Work* (Ian Allan, 1980) that this blastpipe was originally that on SR 'Lord Nelson' No 862, but the dates of removal and fitting do not appear to support this.

Chapter 4

29 *Railway Magazine*, November 1934.
30 *Railway Magazine*, December 1935.
31 *Railway Magazine*, January 1936.
32 *Performance and Efficiency Tests, BR Standard Class 5 2-cylinder 4-6-0 Mixed Traffic Locomotive*, BR Bulletin No 6, May 1953, forms the basis of the calculations, using train resistance figures from *The Measurement of Train Resistance*, H. I. Andrews; Proc Inst Loco E, Vol 237, 1954.
33 *Railway Magazine*, July 1937.
34 Reproduced by Rowledge & Reed, op cit (5), Figs 10 and 23.
35 *Railway Magazine*, August 1940.
36 *Railway Magazine*, July 1938.
37 *Railway Magazine*, August 1938.
38 *Railway Magazine*, December 1937.
39 *Railway Magazine*, November 1964.
40 See *The Locomotive, Railway Carriage & Wagon Review*, 15 July 1935, page 219, for a description and illustrations of these elements.

Chapter 5

41 *SLS Journal*, November 1979.

42 *Railway Magazine*, January/February 1944.
43 *Trains Illustrated*, October 1958.
44 *Chronicles of Steam*, E. S. Cox; Ian Allan, 1967. Chapter IX.
45 A. J. Powell, op cit (4), Fig 2.
46 *Organisation and Control of Locomotive Repairs on British Railways*, R. C. Bond; Proc Inst Loco E, Vol 232, 1953.
47 O. S. Nock, op cit (7), pages 97/98.
48 *Experience with the steel fireboxes of the Southern Region Pacific Locomotives*, M. G. Burrows & A. L. Wallace; Proc Inst Loco E, Vol 262, 1958.
49 *Some Developments in Locomotive Workshop Practice, 1939-1948*, I. C. Forsyth; Proc Inst Loco E, Vol 209, 1949.

Chapter 6
50 *Chronicles of Steam*, E. S. Cox.
51 *Report of the Locomotive Testing Committee on the Locomotive Interchange Trials, 1948*; The Railway Executive, 1948.
52 A. J. Powell, op cit (4), Chapter 6.
53 *The Locomotive Exchanges*; C. J. Allen; Ian Allan, 1949.
54 *Trains Illustrated*, December 1959.
55 *Railway Magazine*, May 1957.
56 *Railway Magazine*, December 1964.
57 *Railway Magazine*, February 1958.
58 *Railway Magazine*, September 1959. Another 96mph was recorded in this area in the same magazine for February 1958.

59 *More Firing Days at Saltley*; Terry Essery; Bradford Barton, 1981. Chapter II.
60 A. J. Powell, op cit (4), Fig 3.
61 *Railway Magazine*, February 1958.
62 *Railway Magazine*, January 1964.
63 *Trains Illustrated*, June 1960.
64 *Railway Magazine*, October 1966.
65 *Railway Magazine*, March 1966.
66 *Railway Magazine*, May 1967.
67 *Railway Magazine*, March 1964.
68 John Clay, in the *Stanier Black Fives* (Ian Allan, 1972) quotes a figure of 1,425EDBHP, but this is patently wide of the mark.
69 *Railway World*, February 1973.

Chapter 7
70 *Locomotive Panorama*, Vol 1, E. S. Cox; Ian Allan, 1965. Chapter V.
71 E. S. Cox, op cit (70), Fig 11.
72 E. S. Cox, op cit (70), Fig 20.
73 A. J. Powell, op cit (4), Fig 9.

Appendix 4
74 *Balancing of Locomotive Reciprocating Parts*, E. S. Cox; Proc Inst Loco E, Vol 165. 1942.

Appendix 8
75 *Developments in Locomotive Testing*; S. O. Ell; Proc Inst Loco E; Vol 235; 1953 and O. S. Nock, op cit (7), Fig 231.

Index